THE SCOOP TROOP

Akaloo 1
Grades 5-6

By
Louis R. Carlozo

Illustrated by
Shawn Finley

The Scoop Troop

Akaloo 1

Grades 5-6

Published in cooperation with Congregational Ministries Publishing, a ministry of the General Assembly Council, Presbyterian Church (U.S.A.).

Page 50: Lyrics © 2006 Louis R. Carlozo, published by Them Apples Music/ASCAP. Used by permission.

Page 71: Lyrics from "Dear God" by Andy Partridge, © 1987 Virgin Music (Publishers) Ltd.

Writer: Louis R. Carlozo

Editors: Becky Weaver, Dawn Rundman, and James Satter

Cover design: Spunk Design Machine

Illustrations: Shawn Finley

ISBN–13: 978-0-8066-5733-2
ISBN–10: 0-8066-5733-2

The paper used in this publication meets the minimum requirements of American National Standard for Information Sciences—Permanence of Paper for Printed Library Materials, ANSI Z329.48-1984.

Manufactured in the U.S.A.

09 08 07 07 06   1 2 3   4 5 6 7 8 9 10

Contents

Meet the Scoop Troop!

● ● ● ● ● ● ● ● ● ● ● ● ● ● ● ● ● ● ● ●

Monica Perez—An adventurous omnivore who has tried pickled pigs' feet on a dare, Monica enjoys hanging out and having fun. With her boisterous laugh and outgoing nature, Monica would much rather be on the beat meeting people and schmoozing than in the office. A great advice columnist as well as an "idea hamster"—the kind of person whose crazy inspirations multiply like fuzzy pets—Monica is clearly the most charismatic person in the newsroom: a creative dynamo who makes things happen. Still, she's a bit of a control freak. She wants to make  sure everything is going well and that everyone gets along, and gets moody whenever the slightest disagreement takes place. Monica's father is a surgeon, and her mother is an English professor, but Monica's life isn't as charmed as it seems. (Her parents divorced when she was six, and she rarely sees her father since he remarried two years ago.)

 **Mark Engstrom**—Mark is funny, a skeptic, and always looking for the odd angle on any story. He's very disorganized but always gets the story in the end. He causes lots of tension by working up to the last possible second on deadline, but he's the one everyone goes to for tips and pointers—even Monica the advice columnist seeks his advice. One on one, Mark has the demeanor of a young philosopher-pastor type. Yet in front of

the group, he has an irresistible compulsion to be the cut-up or clown. Mark may be the brightest of the bunch, and as a result tries to think his way out of any jam. But this has its limits, especially when he has to take a leap of faith, which he often finds terrifying.

Rob Jordan—Rob's dominant personality trait is that he's curious. Also thoughtful and reserved, Rob listens to really loud modern rock and hip-hop on his MP3 headphones, which means that it's hard to get his attention; the other Troopers often have to repeat things for him. Since Rob doubles as the paper's designer and photographer, he thinks visually and usually expresses his ideas with sketches and diagrams—and few words. But occasionally, some random topic—like the history of Chicago's public transportation system—will set him off on a rambling speech that leaves the rest of the staff scratching their heads. He also likes to ask hypothetical questions that lead to some pretty weird discussions/arguments. Here's a sample type of question: "What if Jonah were swallowed by cannibals instead of a whale?" It's just Rob's nature to ask.

Christopher Lewis—A joyful, quasi-hippie type who believes anything is possible, Christopher is borderline naïve, often overwhelmed, and he prays for help a lot. It was his idea to start this newspaper, although he never thought anyone would take it seriously, let alone follow through with it. As the editor, he's in way over his head. He has never done this before and believes in let-

ting everyone get their ideas out before he says anything—and when he does, it's often in the form of a question rather than a directive. Oddly enough, everyone in the group takes his notions seriously (although Mark will get a wisecrack in now and then). Christopher writes songs on an acoustic guitar and often expresses a feeling or idea more profoundly in music than in prose. His ambition: to be someone who rides the rails with a wireless laptop, making money by trading stocks on the Internet.

Wendi Best—A finicky eater who picks even the cheese off her pizza, Wendi is often annoyed by Monica's outgoing nature, which she believes, in her worst moments, is a put-on. Wendi is a doer who believes the only way to put out a newspaper is to sit glued to the desk doing Internet research, making phone calls, and writing like crazy. A product of a conflict-filled home, Wendi uses the work at the paper as a means of escape. She rarely leaves the office and her behavior can often be brash and irrational. But in moments of clarity, she will begrudgingly admit Monica is a great asset to the staff (and even admires Monica at times). Wendi also has a beautiful, bold writing voice, a greyhound—named Ethel—that she got from animal rescue, and three cats.

Mr. George Naynum—The advisor to the paper who also teaches Sunday school at the church where the Scoop Troop meets, Mr. Naynum is nothing short of inspirational. When the staff gets down, he presses them to keep going. When the idea of a newspaper starts to wear thin, he reminds the Scoop Troopers in the most creative of ways how they are making a

difference. In his early 40s, Mr. Naynum has two children, a four-year-old girl and a two-year-old boy. On those rare times when he appears frazzled, it's because of some misadventure with his kids. Still, his ready laugh and clarity of vision make him beloved by all the staff, who sometimes approach him with very personal concerns.

Mainframe—Monica purchased this beat-up, old computer at a garage sale for $20, but for some reason Mainframe, which used to belong to an artificial-intelligence researcher, seems to have a mind of its own. Monica says the researcher sold the computer in a rush to clear out the garage for a move. When Monica went to return it the next day after encountering its "independent streak," the family had moved. For starters, Mainframe will suggest solutions to problems and frustrations by flashing messages on its screen (or talking in a voice that sounds like movie star Donny Sheek), even as Monica and the other staffers grumble to themselves. Mainframe also seems able to read feelings well and sometimes seems to have feelings of its own. (It sometimes appears jealous of newer computer models.) Best of all, Mainframe tries to warns everyone when it feels a crash coming, though it's no less frustrating when it does conk out on a deadline.

YOU—Yes, that's right, you! The Scoop Troopers need all the help they can get. But before we make you part of the team, we need to know a little bit about you. So if you could, please fill out the employment application below.

Name: _____

Age: _____

Hometown: _____

Grade: _____

School: _____

My favorite school subject is: _____

     Because: _____

My least favorite school subject is: _____

     Because: _____

Here are some special talents I have that would make me a great asset to a newspaper:

_____

_____

If you're having trouble thinking of any, that's okay. Here are just a few examples to consider: I work well under pressure; I take great pictures; I'd make an awesome advice columnist; I love to write; I'd make a super cartoonist, and so on.

The one thing I can do better than just about anyone else:

_____

I couldn't believe it when God answered this prayer:

_____

If you could tell people anything about Jesus, what would it be?

_____

The Bible story I enjoy the most is: _____ _____

Because: _____

The Bible story I have the hardest time believing is: _____

_____

Because: _____

These are some special people in my life. Here's who and why:

_____

_____

_____

The one place I dream of visiting some day is: _____

_____

The one thing most people don't know about me (but should!):

_____

_____

_____

My favorite toy as a kid was: _____

My favorite actor/ actress: _____
If you become an entertainment reporter, we'll need to know this!

My favorite musician/music group: _____

I can't believe people like: _____
Fill in an entertainer, TV show, movie, or music group.

Most frequently visited Web site: _____

Why? _____

What are you most passionate about in life? There is no wrong answer here! Just tell us what you love to do, or what you would spend your life doing, if you could, and why:

_____

_____

_____

_____

_____

_____

_____

SCOOP TROOP ALERT

Now look at the Scoop Troop staff lineup. We need you to add a picture of yourself in the empty spot—draw a cartoon or stick figure or attach a picture. Do whatever you want—so long as your mug shot is part of the lineup.

Thanks! Welcome aboard! And now, it's off to your first news meeting...

This is me!

The Scoop Troop

Bible

Let's Get (the Press) Fired Up!

● ● ● ● ● ● ● ● ● ● ● ● ● ●

> *What's so great about the Bible?*
> **It's unique.**

It was obvious by the way he descended into the basement of Shorewood Park Church—his shoulders slightly stooped, a heavy sigh hissing like a deflated tire—that Christopher Lewis would rather be anywhere else than here, off to his first meeting to launch a radical experiment in journalism.

"I shouldn't feel like this," he mumbled to himself. "It was my idea. But I never thought when I blurted it out at youth group that anyone would take it seriously." Then he considered all the possible reasons he'd suggested a weekly newspaper in the first place. To sound important. To impress the girls. To break the awkward silence in the room.

Christopher remembered how the events began just moments before the youth group's last meeting, when Mr. Naynum posed a question to the group.

● ●

"If nobody talks about the incredible stories and history and good news in the Bible, then how is anybody going to know?" asked Mr. Naynum, the youth group's adult leader.

"You'd just assume everyone would know," said Mark Engstrom, who never let an opportunity to make a wisecrack get past him. "There's this guy in an emo band at Parker Middle School, and at their last concert he was wearing this T-shirt that said, 'Jesus is coming. Everyone look busy.'"

Everyone laughed, except Wendi Best. After all, anyone with pink-streaked hair can sympathize with another outsider—emo, goth, marching band geek, you name it. "That's *sooo* funny, Mark," she said. Then she paused and added, "Why should any of this Bible stuff matter to anyone today anyway? I mean, I believe it. I grew up with it. But if I ever tried to discuss it with my friends, they would be like, 'That was so yesterday.' As in way, way thousands of years ago yesterday. Or they'd say, 'When was the last time you saw anyone raised from the dead? Or a miracle?'"

"Great questions," Mr. Naynum said. "So again, how do we get out the good news?"

No one seated in the circle had an answer—or wanted to offer one. Not Rob Jordan, who doodled in his sketch book. Not Monica Perez, who looked like she was going to say something but drew a short breath and held back—not like her at all. Wendi just scratched her scalp until little flakes fell on her shoulder like flurries in a snow globe.

Christopher felt as if the tension rested square on his shoulders. And then: "How about a *Good News-paper* . . ."

There are times in life when words fly off the tongue like spitballs from a straw, and they cannot be withdrawn. And like any good, gooey spitball, this question stuck.

"Excellent!" Mr. Naynum said.

The kids in the room buzzed and everyone nodded—everyone but Christopher. Rob dashed off a quick sketch of a nameplate design and held it up for all to see: *Good Newspaper.* And underneath, this credo à la *The New York Times:* "All the news that's true, we do."

"So when's our first planning meeting?" Mr. Naynum asked.

. . . .

And so it had happened that quickly and decisively. "Impossible," Christopher said to himself as he descended the church stairs. "We're never going to pull this off. I've never written an 'A' paper in English, let alone edited a newspaper."

"You're right," a voice inside him said. *"You'll never do it—not alone, anyway."* Christopher remembered what his uncle, a crusty editor at the *Detroit Free Press* once told him: "A newspaper is a daily miracle." Interesting choice of words for a crabby skeptic with coffee-and-tuna-fish breath: "Daily miracle."

Christopher chewed on that phrase like a comforting wad of cherry gum. And then he thought of something his mom always said, time and again: "God loves an impossible idea." To which Christopher replied to himself, "I sure hope so."

Christopher was so preoccupied when he entered the basement that he didn't notice the time—2:10 P.M. Sunday—or that he was 10 minutes late for the first meeting of the *Good Newspaper.* He walked into the midst of an animated discussion.

"It's not like I've seen it on Oprah's book club," Wendi said.

"And mine doesn't have any pictures in it—no photos, no illustrations, not even a doodle space," Mark added.

"What are you guys talking about?" Christopher asked.

"You're late," Wendi shot back. "How do you expect to run

a newspaper if you're late to the first meeting?"

"But it wasn't my idea . . ." Christopher said.

"As I recall, it was your idea," Wendi said.

"Okay, so the newspaper part was my idea—but it definitely wasn't my idea to actually follow through with it," Christopher replied a bit defensively.

"Maybe," Mr. Naynum said, "we should get back to the question."

"Which is?" Christopher asked.

"What's so great about the Bible?" Rob replied.

"Are you asking me?" Christopher asked.

"No," Rob said. "That's the question. But actually yes—I am asking you."

"And everyone else here ought to try to brainstorm an answer, too," Mr. Naynum said.

"One great thing is that if there's a strong breeze coming through the kitchen, it's heavy enough to keep my homework from blowing off the table," Mark said.

Monica wadded up a piece of notebook paper and winged it at Mark, grazing his left ear. Mark stuck out his tongue and grinned.

"Very mature," Monica said. Then she added, "I can think of lots of great things about the Bible. Maybe we should make a list."

"Great," said Mr. Naynum, stepping up to a dry erase board. "Let's take down some ideas."

SCOOP TROOP ALERT

The Troopers need your help. Take a few minutes to write down some things you think are great about the Bible. When everyone in your group is done, discuss your ideas.

Mr. Naynum looked pleased. "I think we've got enough solid suggestions here to start a regular series for our newspaper. We'll concentrate on one new idea every week for the next few weeks. But I still think we're missing the big idea, the one that could kick off our first issue of this series."

"You're looking for something unique?" Christopher asked.

"That's it!" Monica said. "You're brilliant."

Christopher looked more confused than ever. "I'm lost."

"No, I think Monica's right," Mr. Naynum said. "You're hardly lost. In fact you've found the right answer, even if you stumbled onto it. Care to explain, Monica?"

"Sure," she said. "See, the Bible is unique. And it's unique in so many ways that we could make that the basis for our first editorial. It's a book made up of many books, written by many authors. It contains poetry, wise sayings, and history."

"And it's more widely distributed than any book in the world," Wendi added.

And from there, the ideas began to flow.

SCOOP TROOP ALERT

What do you think is unique about the Bible? Consider categories such as:

- Longevity

- Influence

- Everyday expressions that come from its pages

- Anything else you can think of!

Make your list the basis for a group discussion.

The Truth (and a Dare)

• • • • • • • • • • • •

> What's so great about the Bible?
> **It shapes Christian worship.**

It was early Tuesday evening, and Monica Perez was putting some finishing touches on the latest issue of the *Good Newspaper.* She was seated at Mainframe, her faithful computer that she had donated to the "newsroom"—actually the youth group room in the basement of Shorewood Park Church. "Could you do a spell check?" she typed in. And out came that familiar voice, that soothing voice that sounded exactly like movie star Donny Sheek *(sigh)* that announced an impending detour.

"No can do, Monica," Mainframe replied. "Need to sleep for a bit. I've been on the go all day." Then Mainframe let out a long yawn. "See you in a few," it said—and the screen went black.

How aggravating, Monica thought. And it didn't help that the youth choir was practicing upstairs. Although Monica liked "This Little Light of Mine," she wasn't particularly fond of listening to it 20 times in a row, complete with cracked notes and missed cues. It was like enduring an endless episode of one of those reality show singing contests, but without the flashing lights and screaming audience. "That's good," Monica snickered as she plugged in her headphones and cranked up some tunes. "I'd love to see the choir on that show. Maybe we could get them some glow-in-the-dark robes and…"

Just as Monica was enjoying her little reality-TV fantasy, in walked Wendi Best—not her favorite person, not that Monica hadn't tried again and again to be her friend. And this time, Monica could tell by Wendi's narrow stare that something was up. Something concerning the two of them.

Wendi reached into her backpack, the one covered with about 100 zillion rock-band pins, and pulled out a jar.

"Hi, Wendi," Monica said, with an obviously fake smile. "Nice weather we're having!"

"Oh come on, Monica." Wendi said. "Let's get down to business." She held up the jar, hiding the label from Monica's sight. The contents looked mysterious.

"I heard once that you ate pickled pigs' feet on a dare," Wendi said. "But maybe that was my mistake. Or maybe you took just a bite. Or maybe you switched out the pigs' feet for beef stew."

"So what's your point?" asked Monica, unplugging her headphones.

"You're proud of the fact that you'll try anything—pickled pigs' feet, squirrel, rattlesnake, ostrich. But I'll bet you've never eaten a whole jar of calves' brains before."

"So what's in this for me?" Monica asked.

"Name it," Wendi offered.

Monica mulled it over. *Too easy,* she thought. But this could be fun. "I eat that jar of calves' brains and you put together a special feature for the next issue on Bible Stuff."

"Done," Wendi said, popping open the lid and gingerly handing the jar and a spoon to Monica. Then Monica dipped in, the noise sounding just like what you hear when you're trying to grab a scoop of squishy, lukewarm jelly.

Monica lifted the spoon to her nose. And for show-off effect, she closed her eyes, inhaled deep, smiled, and sighed. Then she took a bite, not just swallowing it, but savoring it, as if it were creamy Swiss chocolate. *"Mmmm!"*

Monica didn't even have to take a second taste before Wendi's complexion turned grayish green. She looked faint. "Stop!" she yelled.

"Sure you don't want a bite?" Monica said, holding out a heaping spoonful. "It tastes kinda like … kinda like brain food! Or cold liver and pudding after you've dropped it in the sand."

Wendi gagged, jamming her right hand against her mouth.

"Deadline's a week from today, sweetie!" Monica cooed.

Just then, the other Scoop Troopers bounded into the newsroom.

"Hey look!" Christopher said, holding up an envelope. "We got a letter from a reader, and the issue hasn't even hit the stands yet. Or should I say the pews?"

"No," Mark said. "Don't say pew until you know for sure people think our newspaper stinks."

"Ha, ha, ha—clunk. That's me laughing my head off," said Wendi in a perfect deadpan.

Rob made a quick sketch and held it up, making a whistling sound that went down in pitch. It was a picture of a bomb.

"Okay, Christopher, so what does the letter say?" Monica asked.

Christopher tore open the envelope and began reading: "Dear *Good Newspaper*: What archeological evidence can be found in the Roman catacombs from the 1st century A.D. that sheds more light on the worship habits of the earliest Christians?"

"Huh?" Monica said.

"Just kidding," Christopher said, grinning sheepishly.

"Spare us and leave the comedy to Mark," Wendi said, "as much as it pains me to say that."

"Oh, Wendi! My biggest fan!" Mark sighed.

Christopher read the letter: "Dear *Good Newspaper:* Everyone tells me that the Bible has shaped the way Christians worship. But I've always wondered how. Could you tell me? Signed, Kevin Moore, age 11."

"Wow," Monica said. "Good question, Kevin." She looked at Wendi. "Looks like you can get started on your feature, Wendi."

Wendi grabbed the letter from Christopher's hand and reread it. "I guess I know what I'll be researching this weekend."

"What feature? Why is Wendi working on it?" asked Mark. Then the jar of calves' brains caught his eye. "And what the HECK is that?

"Never mind," Wendi and Monica both said together.

Wendi set off to find some answers to Kevin's letter.

SCOOP TROOP ALERT

What do you think are some ways the Bible has shaped Christian worship? See if your group can make a list.

Take a look at your group's list and see if you can add anything to Wendi's reply to Kevin's letter.

Here's what Wendi came up with:

The Bible shapes Christian worship in many wonderful ways. First, it contains timeless wisdom and advice in books such as Proverbs. The psalms are eloquent songs to God that show how even the greatest heroes of the Bible, such as David, experienced emotions from despair to hope—and praised God much as we do. It tells stories about God's interaction with humans, ranging from Genesis and the Garden of Eden to the birth of God as an infant in a manger. It collects stories across thousands of years of history, showing how God's relationship with people has changed (kind of like parents watching their children grow up). It is filled with poetry, which shows God is a creative creator, the ultimate artist.

And in telling the story of Jesus, the Bible illustrates how much God loved us. Jesus experienced the same range of hurts, disappointments, joys, and inspirations as we do—and then some. He picked fishermen and ordinary people—not the rich, powerful or super-smart—to carry his message. He did not call his disciples "slaves" or "servants," but "friends." He shared everything that he had. He helped people in trouble and spent time with folks most of us would want nothing to do with, including tax collectors and prostitutes. Then Jesus died on a cross, loving us enough to experience the most humiliating death possible, all so that we no longer have to live in fear of our sins and shortcomings. Also, thanks to his resurrection, we have nothing to fear from death itself. Wow!

The ASK-it-ball Scores

- - - - - - - - - - - - - -

> *What's so great about the Bible?*
> **It has changed history.**

The Scoop Troopers were busy in the church basement looking over page layouts for their next issue. Nothing seemed to gel, and not even Mark's jokes could lighten the mood—nor joking about the lameness of his jokes.

"We need something to pull this issue together," Monica said. "But what could it be? Oh, wait! I'll think of something..."

Just then, everyone turned to hear a loud thumping, as if someone tossed a boulder down the stairs. Not quite, though the sound of Mr. Naynum's bouncing feet and the ball he dribbled made everyone take notice.

"What's with the basketball?" Mark asked Wendi.

Mr. Naynum arched his arms as if taking a jump shot, bent at the knees, and made a nothing-but-net swoosh sound. "Great question, Mark!" he said, "considering the unique journalistic tool I now hold in my hand."

"A basketball?" Mark asked. "What are we gonna cover, fantasy Bible league sports?"

"Not a basketball," Mr. Naynum said, "but an ASK-it-ball!" He threw a chest pass at Mark, who nearly fell off his chair catching it.

"Hey," Mark said, examining the orange ball covered with green, cartoonish question marks. "What's with this?"

"Again, a great question. And that's what the ASK-it-ball is all about." Mr. Naynum walked over, plucked the ball from Mark's hands, and strolled to the center of the room. The Troopers pulled themselves into a makeshift circle.

"Here's how it works," Mr. Naynum said. "When I throw the ball to you, you have to answer the question that was just asked. Then, you ask a question and throw the ball to someone else. Then they have to answer your question and come up with another question before they pass the ASK-it-ball off again."

"Are questions about quantum mechanics fair game?" Christopher asked.

"If that's the topic," Mr. Naynum said. "But just like basketball, ASK-it-ball has its rules. And the main rule of this game is that when you start with a topic, you stick with it—or else you get called for a foul."

"But I'm really bad at sports," Wendi said, sighing.

"Look," Mr. Naynum reassured her, "if you can play catch, you can play ASK-it-ball. It's much more about how nimble your *mind* is than anything else." He dribbled the ball on the tile floor and did a quick pivot to face Rob, who was doodling a page full of question marks. "So folks, what's our topic gonna be?"

The room fell silent. Then Monica spoke up. "We're all really stumped for this next issue of the *Good Newspaper,* and we don't know where to go with it."

"But with a game like this," Christopher said, "we could change the very course of history!"

"That's it!" Monica said.

"Huh?" said Christopher, looking like he'd just heard a sentence uttered in Aramaic.

"History," Monica said, motioning to Mr. Naynum to throw her the ball. "That's what we could focus on. How has the Bible changed HISTORY?"

"That's good, Monica," Mr. Naynum said. "But before you get the ball, is everyone square with the topic?" The Scoop Troopers nodded, including Christopher, who still looked a bit confused. "The topic is 'The Bible has changed history.' Now for the first question: How widespread are the teachings of the New Testament today?"

Mr. Naynum passed the ASK-it-ball to Monica. To everyone's surprise, she caught it with one hand, while typing an Internet search into Mainframe with the other.

"Just a sec," the computer said in its husky Donny Sheek voice. "All right. Says here that about one-third of all people in the world call themselves Christians. That makes it the world's largest religion, so far as I can see. And the best place to read about Jesus is in the Bible."

"Wow," Monica said.

"Is it okay if I sleep now?" Mainframe asked.

"Go ahead, lazybytes," Monica replied. Mainframe started to snore. Monica turned down the speakers. "Hmm. Now, what should I ask? What about art? Did the Bible inspire any great art?"

"Ooh, ooh," Wendi said. "I've got game!" Monica floated a high pass to Wendi, who jumped out of her chair to pull it down. In the process, she dropped the ball.

"That's fine," said Mr. Naynum. "It's not catching the ball that counts so much as scoring a correct answer."

"So I can throw the ball out the window?" Mark said.

"Don't push it," Mr. Naynum said.

"Back to the question," Wendi said. "First off, I learned in music class that Johann Sebastian Bach signed his compositions 'To the glory of God alone.' He wrote a lot of church music, including a Christmas Oratorio and works that were tied to the Lutheran calendar. All the great sculptors and painters of the Renaissance were influenced by the stories of the Bible, too, including Leonardo da Vinci, Michelangelo, Raphael..."

"For some reason that makes me think of turtles doing martial arts. Weird," Mark said sarcastically.

"Turtle this, Mark: How did the Bible bring down an empire?" Wendi made like she was going to wing the ASK-it-ball at Mark's head. As he took cover behind his arms, she lobbed it like ripe peach.

The ball glanced off Mark's shielded face. He grabbed the ball as it rolled across the floor, blushing as everyone laughed. "Got me," he said. "But not on the question."

"Do tell," Wendi said.

"It just so happens I visited Rome with my family last summer, and we went on a tour of the ruins," Mark said. "One thing I learned was that Emperor Constantine made Christianity the Roman Empire's official religion in the fourth century. Only a few hundred years before that, Romans were persecuting Christians by coating them in tar and burning them for torches at garden parties."

"Gross," Wendi said.

"But soon," Mark added, "Christians became so powerful with their teachings that marble from the Forum and the Coliseum was actually quarried to build new churches! That's why they're ruins today. And soon, anyone who *wasn't* a Christian was getting persecuted. Not that two wrongs make a right. Or as they say in Latin, *duo wrongus no makeus uno rightium.*"

"Sounds more like pig latin to me," Wendi said.

Mark twitched his nose and oinked. Then he got ready to pass the ASK-it-ball to...

After 15 minutes of throwing the ASK-it-ball around, the Scoop Troopers were loose and limber, like a team ready to hit the court and win.

"Let's start writing and designing!" Christopher said. "We've got another issue to put out!" He was excited, but in the back of his head, he couldn't help but think, *How long can we keep this up?*

He kept the nagging thought to himself, and instead said this: "But before we get to work, there's one person who has yet to touch the ASK-it-ball. And that would be…"

"Mr. Naynum!!!" the group answered in unison.

"Okay, okay," Mr. Naynum said. "Give me your best."

"Mr. Naynum," Christopher began. "I thought I saw you upstairs hugging the new choir director. Care to shed any light on that?"

"OOOHHH!" the Troopers crooned.

Mr. Naynum caught the ball, laughing. He replied: "That, sir, is a foul. She's my cousin."

SCOOP TROOP ALERT

Here's an ASK-it-ball question for the group to bounce around: How has the Bible impacted North American history? The Scoop Troopers are stumped and need your help. If you are to think about and expand on categories such as these:

• The opening of hospitals and universities.

• The end of slavery.

• Court and post-election swearing-in rituals. (Hint: What do they swear on?)

• The Civil Rights movement of the 1950s to 1960s.

• Today's push to stop the spread of HIV/AIDS.

Generations of Generations of...

● ● ● ● ● ● ● ● ● ● ● ● ● ●

> *What's so great about the Bible?*
> **It links generations locally
> and across time.**

"Okay, you guys," Christopher Lewis said as the Scoop Troopers settled in for another meeting. "Now that we've got a few issues of the *Good Newspaper* under our belts..."

Mark Engstrom interrupted, as only Mark could: "Would those by chance be BIBLE belts?"

"Mark," Wendi said, "I would groan. Really, I would. But the attention would just encourage you to keep cracking more of those awful jokes."

"Why, thank you," Mark said.

"Whaddaya mean 'thank you'?" Wendi asked.

"In its original sense," Mark replied, " the word *awful* meant 'to be full of awe.' A most appropriate reaction to my incredible wit."

"From this day forward," Wendi grumbled, "I will make it my purpose in life to develop a whipped cream cannon that fires automatically at the sound of one of Mark's jokes."

"Um, could we get back to business?" Christopher asked.

"Arrrrrgrh!" Rob bellowed.

"And what's *your* problem with getting back to business?" Christopher asked.

"No, no, no!" Rob countered. "That's not it."

"I knew it," Wendi said. "It was Mark's jokes. You know, I feel your pain and…"

"No, that's not it either," Rob said. He held up a drawing with his right hand for the group to see, a sprawling scribble that resembled a vine gone crazy, or a flow chart belched from a blender. Hundreds of branching lines converged at the bottom of the page, and the margins of the page were crowded with calculations, scrawled and scratched out.

The group stared at it for a while in silence.

"I've got it!" Mark said. "It's Rob's abstract representation of the book of Numbers."

"Or the new 'new math,'" Monica said.

"No, it's his proposal for the youth group budget," Wendi said.

"Hmmm," Mainframe said. "This program has performed an illegal operation and will be shut down."

"Or is it a guide to understanding Rob's mind at work?" Christopher asked.

"Perhaps," Mr. Naynum said, looking over at Rob, "perhaps we should give Rob a chance to tell us what it is. Or is that too novel a concept for this troop?"

Rob cleared his throat. "Okay. You ready?"

There are times when the usual order of things in the universe overturns, when the quiet kid gives way to the stirring blabbermouth inside. All the Scoop Troopers knew that on most days, Rob Jordan was as quiet as a monk in a monastery. But just as a hungry lizard is given away by a sly flick of the tongue, Rob's clearing of the throat signaled one of his classic "can't-wrap-my-head-around-it" speeches coming on.

"Ready," Christopher said. "I think."

"So I got to thinking," Rob began. "I have two parents, right?"

"Unless the angel Gabriel visited your mom too," Mark offered.

"As opposed to Mark," Wendi said, "who was found floating in a basket and taken to live in the palace of the Funny Pharaoh."

"Seriously, I have two parents, and I'm 11. And my parents each have two parents, my grandparents. That means that if each generation equals about 30 years, there are six people going back 71 years who are responsible for my birth, not counting brothers, sisters, aunts, uncles, or cousins. So what I decided to do was create a flowchart-tree that tries to estimate exactly how many people are directly involved in my creation —to see how far back I could take it."

"And what did you find out?" Mr. Naynum asked.

"It was all so simple at first!" Rob said. "If each parent has two parents, then the numbers just double with each generation. I have two parents, four grandparents, eight great-grandparents and 16 great-great grandparents. That took me back to about the year 1875. And so far, easy to grasp, right? But then when I took the numbers further back in time, things got a bit overwhelming."

"How so?" Christopher inquired.

"Let's go back to the year 1695," Rob said. "Now keep in mind that all I did was assume that every parent had two parents, and that each set of parents had a kid at about age 30, which is probably being generous, since people tended to have children at earlier ages long ago. That means that just before 1700, there are—get this—1024 people in my direct line who were probably alive at that time."

"Wow," Mark said.

"What are you so 'awwwed' about, Mark?" Wendi asked. "You're an android, built from the finest auto salvage parts."

"Hey, Wendi," Mark responded, "is that pink hair or were you attacked by a value-pack of bubble gum on the way to church?"

"C'mon, let Rob finish!" Monica said.

"I should've stopped at the year 1695, but I couldn't," Rob said. "I went back to 1395 and that's when I hit the one-million-person mark."

"Wait ... that's got to be wrong," Christopher said.

"That's what I thought," Rob said. "So I checked the math and checked it again, and again, but it seemed to come out the same every time. And the year 1245? That's about 33 million people, all my direct ancestors! I didn't even dare go back to the time of Jesus. I was afraid my mind would fry. But then, something really scary occurred to me."

"And that was?" Mr. Naynum said.

"How could all those people be my great-great grandparents of parents of parents, and so on, if everyone pretty much descended from Adam and Eve?" Rob asked. "Or at the very least, descended from a lot fewer people than are alive today?"

"Yikes," Monica said.

"I have a headache," Wendi said.

> ### SCOOP TROOP ALERT
> The Scoop Troopers are mentally fatigued after hearing all about Rob's exercise with his ancestors. Can you help them brainstorm some thoughts about how the Bible links generations? (Turn the page for more ideas.)

"And I have an idea," Monica added, "for the theme of our next issue: generations."

Monica's idea settled the Scoop Troop into the groove it needed to get cracking on another issue. Each member decided to write a short piece on how the Bible's values had been passed down through the years in their respective families.

Rob calmed down enough to toss out his tree sketch and start fresh on a new illustration of a Bible being handed off like a baton.

Everyone seemed to be chugging along, scribbling away into their note pads.

Everyone, that is, except Wendi.

Mr. Naynum noticed that she looked agitated, near tears. He walked over and sat beside her. "Are you all right?" he whispered to her.

"Mr. Naynum, can we talk after the meeting is over? Please?" Wendi asked.

Mr. Naynum nodded his head. He had a feeling he knew what this was going to involve, knowing the kind of home Wendi Best came from.

SCOOP TROOP ALERT

Here are three ways the Bible links generations:

- The Bible gives details about generations. There are many places where certain genealogies are traced (like the ancestry of Jesus, outlined in Matthew 1:1-17).

- The values in the Bible are timeless. They've been passed down for thousands of years without losing any of their value or truth. What Bible values or sayings can you think of that are still used today?

- The Bible has an important role in YOUR history. How have its values shaped your life and the lives of your family members? If you have a chance, talk to some older relatives to learn the important lessons they were taught from the Bible.

Wendi's Story, God's Word

• • • • • • • • • • • • • •

> *What's so great about the Bible?*
> **It is the word of God.**

There were times in her heart of hearts when Wendi Best felt like a freak. While she loved her church and took solace in the idea that God loved her, she also found it all too easy to imagine that other kids around her—especially in the Scoop Troop—had their acts together. And that she didn't.

Sure, everyone respected her because of her no-nonsense demeanor and unique sense of style. Who would mess with a sharp-tongued rocker in high black boots and pink hair? But to her, it seemed the other Troopers all boasted elusive gifts that she lacked. Mark appeared so carefree. Rob was the walking definition of creativity. Christopher came across as the essence of laid-back. And Monica: how Wendi wished she could be as appealing, smart, and bubbly as Monica. She'd die if Monica ever found that out.

Wendi always felt this way after enduring another one of her parents' fights. At least they didn't drag her into it this time—for that she was thankful. But the way they argued, the muffled shouts burrowing through the walls of their bedroom and into hers: It sounded like voices from a nightmare. She could feel the harshness in their exchanges, the cutting phrases, such as, "This marriage feels like a prison" and

"So when did you stop caring?"

Most times, Wendi could put up a brave front. After years of this, she was tough. But when all the Scoop Troopers were asked to write about the love of generations passed on via the Bible, her façade cracked and she felt broken. She decided to reach out.

When the other Troopers filed out after the meeting, Mr. Naynum walked up to Wendi and sat on the floor in front of her. "Let's make this as easy as we can," he said. "You talk. I'll listen."

For just a moment, Monica lingered at the top of the church basement steps. She wanted to listen in—not to collect gossip but to see what might be bothering Wendi. The two had a knack for getting on each other's nerves, that was for sure. But in this moment Monica found her heart softening. Wendi was troubled, and she could sense it. As Wendi began to speak, Monica softly stepped away.

"I don't know," Wendi said, sighing. "My parents. They just fight. All the time. And I can tell they don't love each other. Last night, they were at it until three in the morning. I just stuffed the pillow over my head and tried to block it out, but I couldn't. I was shaking. Angry. Sad."

Mr. Naynum nodded.

"I look at all the other kids around me, and I can't imagine that any of them go home to anything like what I have to face," Wendi continued. "I feel so alone. And it's not like I can go to my parents for sympathy, either. They're too busy fighting with each other."

"What about the rest of your family?" Mr. Naynum asked.

"I'm an only child," Wendi said. Then she started crying, her eyes moist with sadness and rage. "Sometimes I wonder if I'm the reason they fight so much. Maybe things were better before I came along."

Mr. Naynum walked over to his desk and grabbed a tissue

box. He handed it to Wendi. "Wendi Best," he said, "anyone who knows you knows that you're a very bright, spirited person. I've never met your parents, but I'm certain that God made you special. And I'm all too familiar with what it's like to come from a less-than-perfect home."

"Really?" Wendi said.

"You're talking to a man who has met his father once," Mr. Naynum said. "And that one time, he was drunk and could hardly stand. To this day, I have no idea whether he's alive or dead." Mr. Naynum drew a breath and continued: "You see, Wendi, our parents are people and sometimes they struggle with very real problems that have nothing to do with us, even though it's easy to get that impression."

"I hear what you're saying. It just doesn't feel that way right now," Wendi said. "But I do want to know what you think I should do."

"I'm your youth group leader, and I'll listen whenever you want to talk," Mr. Naynum said. "And I can tell you where you can start getting more help for yourself. Talk to your guidance counselor at school. Talk to the pastors here at church. No one's hit you or threatened you, have they?"

Wendi shook her head no.

"Good. And there's also one other thing you can do: Don't hide your lamp under a bushel. Put it on a lamp stand. You're a great writer. Use your words to help pull you through."

"I don't understand. I honestly need some help here," Wendi said.

"Jesus knows, in a very real sense, what you are going through," Mr. Naynum said. "Talk about a man who was alone; at the end, even his best friends deserted him. Hanging on the cross, Jesus wondered if God had forgotten about him. Yet he stayed true to his promises. He honored God's word. Jesus *was* God's word."

The faintest trace of a smile formed on Wendi's face.

"Don't forget your Bible, Wendi. It's times like these when you'll discover one more thing that makes it amazing. It's the Word of God. Collected in all those books you'll find the wisdom of the ages, prophesies that point to Jesus as the Prince of Peace. You'll read about people struggling with burdens much as you are, and discover prayers to take you through the darkest of valleys."

"I have an idea," Wendi said.

Mr. Naynum looked pleased. "Now you're talking. What is it?"

"I'd like to write a story about God redeeming the situation I'm in now. Sort of using God's word to inspire my words. What do you think?"

"I think that's awesome," Mr. Naynum said. "So awesome that I'm going to give you some private time to write to your heart's content." He picked up his jacket and put it on. "And if you get stuck, Wendi, you don't need the ASK-it-ball, or to do an Internet search on Mainframe."

"Only Monica knows how to work that crazy computer without crashing it," Wendi said.

"If you get stuck," Mr. Naynum said, heading up the stairs, "look for words in the Word."

SCOOP TROOP ALERT

You can use your words to encounter God's word too! While Wendi gets started, write a story, true or fictitious, based on how the Word of God has made a difference in your life. It doesn't matter if it's based on a huge event or something subtle—but heed the advice of Anton Chekhov, whose play *The Seagull* tells us to write freely so that the words flow from the heart.

Wendi's Story

THE DREAM HOME

. . . .

It was that sound again, the sound of my parents fighting. As I heard their sharp words claw through my bedroom wall, I pulled the comforter over my head and curled up like an infant. I just wished it would all stop.

"Please, Jesus," I prayed. "I know you're there. I want things to be different. I want there to be love." Over and over I prayed it, until the words soothed me to sleep.

Moments later a light flooded under my door, jolting me awake. It felt as if silvery cool raindrops had splashed across my forehead. Had I slept minutes? Hours? Half a day? I couldn't tell, though I felt well rested. I thought someone left the hallway light on, so I went out to shut it off. When I opened the door, I was hit by a brilliance that outshone anything I'd ever seen. But my eyes didn't hurt. And on the floor was a neatly folded card, with fancy writing on it. The card said: "Go to the kitchen."

I went down to my kitchen, only it had been transformed into a formal dining room, like the kind you might see at the White House. And at the end of a long table was a chair that had my name on it, and a breakfast of strawberry-banana pancakes, two strips of crispy bacon, and fresh-squeezed orange juice. My favorite. Yum.

After breakfast, I decided to explore. My house was now a mansion, and the living room had a ceiling high enough for volleyball. Everywhere I saw books, puzzles, games, and my favorite stuffed animals. And on the game table was another card. It said: "What would you like to play?"

"I don't care," I answered. "I just want everyone to get along. No screaming. No yelling. No fighting. Let's just all take care of each other and..."

I couldn't even finish the sentence before all of my stuffies came to life. Some bears played with building blocks. A few dolls tidied up the dollhouse. I challenged my favorite bear, Bonkers, to a game of tic-tac-toe and almost won. I reached for the remote to turn on the HUGE-screen TV. Then a message flashed across the screen: "What makes you feel most alive?"

I love to write, I thought to myself. *I want to create stories that make people laugh and think, with strange and funny characters. I want to inspire people and give them hope.*

Before I knew it, I was INSIDE the TV. And Oprah herself—YESSS!—was asking me about my brand new children's book, *Pinto Bean Billy and the Chili Bowl of Faith.* When the interview was over, the applause roared as loud as the sea, and the spotlights cast a glare over me until I felt wrapped in white fog. As the sound died down, I blinked, and there I stood back in my bedroom. Standing across from me was a man in a flowing white robe that shimmered like a sheet of diamonds. I did not have to see the wound in his side to know who it was. And then he spoke:

"Wendi, do you need a hug?"

I sobbed, throwing my arms around him. My tears fell. "Why do they fight?" I asked.

Jesus said nothing. But he held me and did not let go.

And then I woke up. My comforter was damp, as if I had cried myself to sleep. I bolted downstairs. Same old kitchen with the dead fly trapped behind the wall clock glass. Same old living room with aluminum foil wrapped on the tip of TV antenna. But when I went back to my room, I noticed one thing that was different. It was a folded card, sitting on my desk, its message written in the most handsome script. And it read:

Dearest Wendi,

Thank you for taking a tour of my mansion. Do your best to live by my Word, even if others do not. Follow the passions I have planted in your heart and look for ways to use them to help others. And don't forget to eat your breakfast. Remember: I love you. I make my home in your heart.

Studying for the Test of Time

• • • • • • • • • • • • • •

> *What's so great about the Bible?*
> **It has been studied for thousands of years.**

It was a Wednesday afternoon with no real work to do on the *Good Newspaper* for a few days yet. Still, some Scoop Troopers decided to camp out after school in the Shorewood Park Church basement. It offered them sanctuary of a different sort: a comfortable place to hang out and work on any project. All you had to do was tune out choir practice upstairs—which admittedly wasn't always easy. Monica was cracking the books for a science midterm.

"How long do you suppose you'd have to study for a test if all you've been doing until now is taking very good class notes, but not much of the reading?" she asked Christopher. Christopher had studying on his mind, too. His history test was tomorrow, and he had some catching up to do.

"I don't know," he replied. "But my guess is that you wouldn't want to take a chance on what's on the exam and what's not. Read as much as you can."

"I was afraid you'd say that," Monica said, sighing.

Just then, Mark bounded down the steps. "Hey, guys," he said. "Since when did this become a study hall?"

"And what are you doing here?" Monica responded.

Mark took off his backpack, unzipped it, and pulled out a math book. "Well," he said, "It is midterm week, is it not?"

"Did someone say midterms?" It was Wendi, sliding down the banister rail with an armful of notebooks. "And did I ever mention how much I don't like English class?"

"But you love to write," Mark said.

"That doesn't mean I have to get into verb tenses and predicates and direct objects and gerunds and all that stuff," Wendi said. "I'm sure Shakespeare didn't sit down and say, 'Hmmm. Let me see. To be or not to be. No, Hamlet can't say that because it's bad grammar. It's—gasp!—a fragment.'"

"My sister says that of all the things she's learned at college so far, the most valuable have been how to cook, do laundry, and change the oil in her car," Mark said. "But when she walks out of an exam for something like calculus, she forgets everything in about an hour."

"Not to change the subject," Christopher said, "but isn't it strange everyone is here?"

"Ooohhh!" said Mark, waving his hands as if it were a spooky coincidence.

"Everyone except Rob," Monica said. "But what does he have to study for? That kid has a photographic memory."

"Maybe because he draws everything," Wendi noted. "He's like a walking dry erase board…"

Before Wendi could finish her thought, Rob appeared at the top of the steps, holding a Latin language instruction book. The look of worry on his face spoke volumes.

"Greetings, Emperor Roberius," Mark said. "Your loyal subjects want to know: Thumbs up? Or thumbs down?"

"At this rate, I'd consider tutoring from Pontius Pilate," Rob said. "It's gonna take me 1,000 years of studying this before I get it."

"Which is what he always says before he walks into class and aces the test anyway," Wendi said, rolling her eyes.

"Just imagine if you did have to study something for 1,000 years," Christopher said. "What would that be like?"

"Oops, he's done it again!" Monica said.

"I don't get it," Christopher said. "I just don't get it. What did I do this time?"

"You've given us another topic for our next issue of the *Good Newspaper,*" Monica said.

"But I'm here to study, not to…" Christopher replied.

"Just a five-minute study break, okay?" Monica said. "The Bible: It's been studied for thousands of years. Just think about a thousand years from now. Will anybody be reading the Harry Potter books? Or anything from Oprah's book list?"

"Hey! Watch what you say about Oprah," Wendi said.

"Just think," Monica continued. "Go back to a time way before libraries or computers or printing presses—any of that. And somehow, all of the books of the Bible managed to come together and stay intact. Those verses have inspired kings and given hope to the poor. Its text is so sacred that it's been hand copied by monks. There must've been something incredible in its pages for people to be drawn to it again and again for centuries."

"Almost like it's alive," Rob said.

"You could say its wisdom and stories come to life every time someone picks it up and takes it to heart," Christopher added.

"I couldn't have said it better," Monica said, smiling at Christopher, who grew flush.

"Okay," said Christopher, trying to regain his composure. He stood up from his seat, stumbling slightly. Monica had to bite her tongue to keep from giggling. "So we're here to study, right? No work on the newspaper, right? We'll just save this idea for our regular meeting and work on it then. Right? RIGHT?"

"Right," everyone replied. Christopher sat down and opened his book. "Good," he said. And he began to skim through the stages of photosynthesis one more time. *Too bad I can't practice what I preach,* he thought. *I've got a whole bunch of ideas on how we could talk about the Bible and why people have studied it for so long.* He looked around the room and saw that everyone was scribbling in their binders.

Strange, he thought. *No one writes in a notebook when they're reading for an exam. Not usually, anyway.*

Christopher cleared his throat to speak: "So ... who wants to share their idea first?" And the church basement filled with laughter.

SCOOP TROOP ALERT

If you were to spend time studying the Bible, what books would you concentrate on and why? Is it because they are among your most favorite? Or is it because you know the least about them? Which Bible stories have you gone back to again and again, and why? What do you get from them? Write down your thoughts and share them with the group.

Christopher's Song of Connection

> *What's so great about the Bible?*
> **It connects Christians around the world.**

It was about 11 P.M., and Christopher Lewis knew he should be in bed. He'd said good night to his parents an hour ago. But he just couldn't sleep. Maybe he was still keyed up from studying for his history exam; he drank a lot of coffee to stay awake. *I would love it if there was a coffee shop somewhere close,* he thought. *Like in our basement.*

Ah, coffee. Which reminded him: the Shorewood Park Church coffeehouse was coming up in a week. It had totally slipped Christopher's mind! "Rats," he said to himself, sighing. "I told them I'd perform an original song, but I don't have anything ready."

Not ready to go to sleep anyway, Christopher pulled out his electric guitar from under the bed, plugged it into his amp, and strapped on his headphones so he wouldn't wake up anyone in the house. He lay back on the bed and began to strum chords as if in a waking dream. C. G. F. And again: C. G. F. Simple stuff, but he liked the feel of it. But what would he write his song about? The first thing that came to mind was a news report he saw earlier in the evening. It was about the AIDS crisis in Africa. The spread of the disease alarmed him, and he knew some people at church talked about helping out.

He heard them saying something about how many Christians lived in Africa: How could Americans turn their backs on brothers and sisters in Christ?

It was a heavy topic, to be sure. But what resonated with Christopher—and began to drive his creative wheels—was a beautiful thought and an awesome responsibility: All Christians everywhere around the world are connected. Connected by the Bible. Connected by the blood of Christ. Connected in faith. *We can't turn our backs on each other,* Christopher thought. Exactly. And he began to sing softly over the chords:

We have all got to live here together
We have all got to live here together
Don't turn your back very long
Or it will all be gone...

Once he had that, the first verse came easily...

Everybody's shouting, trying to be heard
No wonder no one understands a word
And yet we're told to love each other
As we have been loved
Revival...
I read it in the Bible...

Then came the chorus. Writing the rest of the song, Christopher would say later, was painfully easy. Easy as if it had written itself, with help from a Higher Creator. Painful in that Christopher felt the weight of his own sin as he finished up. "For the price of two venti espressos," he wrote in his journal, "I could've bought HIV medication for someone in Africa. To think: I know I'll pass my history test, but I feel like I flunked another."

SCOOP TROOP ALERT

Every major newspaper has an arts section. Inspired by Christopher, the Scoop Troopers are going to create art that centers on the theme of the Bible and connection. Your assignment: create something! It can be anything—a poem, photograph, drawing, essay, short story, song, or painting—as long as it reflects the theme of Christian connection.

In your time as a group, discuss what you'd like to create, and talk about ways that the Bible connects Christians worldwide. Think about:

How its themes go beyond language and culture.

How it can create common morals and laws.

How it teaches us to care for each other despite our differences.

Troopers: For more information about the AIDS crisis in Africa, visit: www.data.org

The Old, the New, the Bridge between the Two

1st Century

> *What's so great about the Bible?*
> **The Old and New Testaments are connected.**

Most likely it was Rob Jordan's crazy family tree sketch that set Monica off on her latest round of surfing the Internet. To be sure, she had always wondered about the people in her family who had come before her—what they looked like, what their lives were like, the world they grew up in. She sat at Mainframe, plugging away at the keyboard as if she were pounding out a piano concerto.

"Okay, Mainframe," Monica said as she dashed off a few more keystrokes. "Our goal is the 1800s. Based on the information we've already uncovered, and what I've saved on your hard drive, can we do a search for people who came from my father's side of the family?"

Mainframe yawned.

"HELLO!" Monica said. "This is my family we're talking about here. Does that bore you or something? Remember, you were just a lonely pile of parts sitting in a cardboard box when I found you at that garage sale…"

"Relax," Mainframe said in a suave Donny Sheek voice. "I was yawning because we've been at this all afternoon. I've been running searches and calculations non-stop for the last three hours. Don't you have someplace you'd rather be, like

| 15th Century | 17th Century | 21st Century |

outside playing dodgeball?"

"Dodgeball?" Monica said, rolling her eyes.

"Or whatever it is you play," Mainframe added.

"This," Monica said firmly, "is my play."

Mainframe sighed.

"So what can you come up with?" Monica said. The whirr and clicking of Mainframe's hard drive indicated that it was working on the query.

"Just a sec. Okay. I pulled this document from a public library archive in New Mexico. It dates from around 1865, if I'm reading the date correctly. The man pictured, standing next to the loaded-down burro, would appear to be in your paternal ancestry, as his last name is Perez, and he resided in an area your family is known to have inhabited at one time."

New Mexico, Monica thought. She knew her grandfather had lived there for a while when he was as a boy. He lived in the town of Gallup, but not before moving soon to Los Angeles. There weren't any family stories she knew of about Perezes in New Mexico.

Mainframe continued: "Name: Salvador Perez. Age at the time of the photo: Approximately 36. Occupation: Farmer."

As Monica stared at the sepia-tone photograph, she could see little resemblance between herself and the man pictured. A short, dumpy-looking farmer with two missing front teeth? What could *he* possibly have to do with her?

"Seems there's a record of a letter here too, if you want me to search for it," Mainframe offered.

"That's okay," Monica said. "Why don't you sleep for a bit, and we'll get back to this later?"

"Are you sure?" Mainframe asked.

"Yeah," Monica said.

"If you insist," the computer replied. And with that the screen went dark, Mainframe's cool banter giving way to the sound of snoring.

Christopher had been seated nearby, working on an editorial for the *Good Newspaper*. For the most part, he was able to tune out Monica and her most unusual computer as they conversed. But the last bit—and especially the resignation in her voice—caught his attention.

"What's wrong, Monica?" he asked.

"It's this family tree stuff," Monica said, turning her chair toward Christopher. "I know this sounds really petty, but I thought when I went back into my ancestry, I'd find all these successful people. Politicians. Artists. Authors. At this point, I'd settle for a steamship captain."

"As opposed to?"

"Well, take the guy I just found: a) he doesn't look a thing like me, and b) he's like this scrubby-looking, dirt-poor farmer. It's bad enough that my one grandpa worked in a canning factory his whole life, and the other one was a gardener for some rich California banker. I'm going back in time but I'm just not finding anything that gives me a sense of feeling ... well ... important."

"I see," Christopher said.

"I know," Monica sighed. "I'm like the most terrible human being to walk the planet, right? Spoiled rotten. A celebrity wannabe."

"No, no, no," Christopher said. "I don't think that at all. But what I do think is that you're failing to see the connection here—the connection between your ancestors and you."

"Okay," Monica said, getting curious. "What do you mean?"

"Take my mom's family, for example," Christopher said. "They came from southern Italy. My grandfather moved here when he was 18. His family was dirt poor, because they came from a small seaside village called Petrizzi, where there wasn't any work for young men. So he and his two older brothers scraped together whatever money they had, tied up all their possessions into a couple of sacks and set sail for America."

"When should I start up the violins?" Monica asked with a grin.

"Come on, stay with me," Christopher said. "So they got here and headed to Philadelphia, where they found jobs right away. They sent money back to Italy, and said they'd be back in a couple of years if everything went well. But it went better than well, way better than they could've ever expected."

"How so?" Monica asked.

"They were able to buy homes and start their own families. In the United States, they lived like kings. And even though they never lost touch with their family, they never went back to live in Italy, either."

"Nice story," Monica said. "But what's your point?"

"Simple: If not for them, and the sacrifices they made, I wouldn't have the life I have today. You see, Monica," Christopher said, "there's a very clear connection between their lives and mine. The dreams of their generation, you could say, became realities for me and my family."

Monica nodded.

"And I don't think they would've been so focused on all of

that if it hadn't been for their faith," Christopher added.

"My grandfather knew his Bible; he knew that the promises of the Old Testament were fulfilled by Jesus in the New Testament. He believed deep down that the seeds he planted would mature and grow into something wonderful—even if he didn't get to see it." Christopher paused for a moment.

Just then, Mainframe butted in: "So, Monica, do you want to see that letter?"

"Mainframe!" Monica said. "I thought you were asleep!"

"Well, even a computer can *pretend* to be asleep," Mainframe replied. "Anyway, here's a printout."

Monica walked over to the printer and picked up the single sheet. She read it aloud. "It says: 'This letter is typical of those written by Western laborers in the late 19th century, and has been translated from the original Spanish,' " Monica began to read:

My Dearest Amelia,

It humbles me to think how much I am at the mercy of forces I cannot control. I wait for rain and it does not come. I run my hands through what was once rich soil and find myself sifting through dust. With the meager crops that have sprung up, I live in constant fear that animals or thieves will take them away. Sometimes it is too much for me to bear. We have sacrificed so much for this small parcel, and now it is all that we have.

My solace is that my God will continue to watch over us, as he watched over our ancestors in ages past. And when we have passed on, I pray that whatever we have grown here will feed and nourish our descendants for generations to come. Please continue to hold on and care for our children. I will send for you from Juarez as soon as I can afford to pay for safe passage. Send my love to your mother.

With all of my heart,

Salvador

Monica stood silent for a moment. She felt ashamed and proud at the same time—ashamed for her own attitude, yet proud of the spirit that coursed through the blood of her rediscovered ancestor. And, she hoped, through her. "Mainframe? Can you print out a picture of Salvador for me?" Monica asked.

"Already done," Mainframe said. "The picture's coming out now."

SCOOP TROOP ALERT

When Monica shared her story with the others, it sparked a lively discussion about the connections between family members past and present. Similar links, they soon realized, united people in the Old and the New Testament. Although hundreds of years separate the two, the Old Testament creates the foundation on which the New Testament rests. Here are some examples:

- Prophesy of a Messiah in Isaiah and Jesus' birth.

- Suffering in Genesis and Jesus' suffering on the cross.

- Adam, the first man, is created and Jesus, the Son of Man, is born.

Take one or two people from the Old Testament such as Adam and Eve, Noah, Moses, Daniel, or Jonah. Imagine they have been transported to the New Testament. Then think about how a story they were involved in might change if it took place in the New Testament instead of the Old. How would they react to the good news of Jesus Christ? Write down some ideas and share them with your group.

God

The Very Picture of Hope

• • • • • • • • • • •

> What does God do
> when bad things happen?
> **God brings hope.**

Behind every great newspaper, there is a staff. And the five kids who made up the *Good Newspaper* at Shorewood Park Church decided it was high time to take a staff photo. Everyone dressed in their favorite threads.

Wendi Best put an extra streak of pink in her spiked hair, polished her black boots and pierced 10 more safety pins through her jean jacket.

Christopher Lewis, the editor, insisted on bringing his acoustic guitar. He wore his most comfortable pair of faded jeans and jean jacket. With his long hair tumbling down, he looked more like a 1970s teen idol than a 21st-century kid—which was how he liked it.

Monica Perez, the resident idea hamster, wore her lime-green turtleneck and a chic, black skirt. Her straight black hair was parted down the center.

With his large sketch pad tucked under one arm, Rob Jordan gave one last spit-shine to his glasses, distinguished by their oversized ebony frames and squared lenses. And while he didn't tell anyone, the quiet, talented artist smoothed a coat of moisturizer to the top and sides of his shaved head.

And finally, Mark Engstrom—the tall boy with blonde bangs—was decked out in his bookish best: wire-framed specs, a red-and-yellow striped rugby shirt, and freshly pressed khakis. Still, a wad of paper jutted from his back pocket—notes left over from his English class. The only person missing was the *Good Newspaper* advisor, Mr. George Naynum.

"Where is he?" Christopher wondered aloud. "How are we going to take a picture without him?"

"We can always get someone else to squeeze the shutter," Mark cracked.

"No, you goof," Wendi said. "Christopher means that Mr. Naynum should be in the picture. But you could always take the picture for us. After all, what's the loss if *you're* not in it?"

"How can I go on," Mark said, holding the back of his hand against his forehead to feign sadness and hurt, "knowing that the incomparable Wendi Best thinks of me as mere worm sweat? Oh, I know! I'll just ignore her. Like everyone else does."

"Mark! Wendi!" Christopher cut in, clearly annoyed. "Can you guys just knock it off for a second? This is serious. Mr. Naynum knew about the shoot. It's not like him to blow it off without saying anything. Something must be up."

The group milled about in confusion near the camera until Wendi spoke up. She was hesitant: "Um ... I don't know if I'm supposed to say anything. And I'm definitely not 100-percent sure of what's going on. But I think I might have an idea where Mr. Naynum is."

"Why didn't you say something earlier? We've been waiting for half an hour now!" Christopher said.

"Like I said, I'm not sure where he is exactly—and I was hoping he would get here," Wendi replied. "But yesterday, I stopped at the church to pick up some school books I'd left behind on Sunday. And I bumped into Mr. Naynum on the way out. He seemed really upset."

"Go on," Christopher said.

"I asked him what was up, and he told me that his mother was sick. Something about Parkinson's disease, and that he was going to visit her in the hospital."

All Christopher could say was, "Oh."

"I don't know if you know this," Monica said, "but Mr. Naynum grew up without a father. His mother was everything to him. She kept him safe from the street gangs as a kid. She didn't just haul him off to church on Sundays, she showed him what God's love looked like by setting an example and showing him how special he was."

"How do you know all this?" asked Wendi, sounding a touch jealous. She thought she was the only one who knew about Mr. Naynum's past.

"My dad was his doctor for a while, and they got to be friends," Monica said. "Of course, I don't see *my* dad much these days, either. You think he would've learned something from talking to Mr. Naynum."

"So what else, Wendi?" Christopher asked.

"When I saw him, he smiled. It wasn't like it was forced; he said he was glad to see me but that he had to run out to see his mom in the hospital. I asked him if there was anything I could do. 'Pray,' he said. Then I asked if he was worried. 'Why worry?' he told me. 'This is all in God's hands. And no matter what happens, God is going to bring hope. Somehow, some way.'"

"Well then," Mark said. "Why wait?"

Rob knew exactly what Mark was talking about. He opened up his sketch pad and made a makeshift banner with big letters. It said: HOPE.

"A backdrop," Rob said. "For the picture. We'll give a copy of the picture to Mr. Naynum."

"Hey, Rob," Wendi said. "One more thing. Do you think you could do a quick sketch of Mr. Naynum for me?"

Rob's pencil ran across the page in rapid strokes, the sound of lead against paper filling an otherwise silent room. Everyone watched as if gathered around a sidewalk artist. In five minutes, the portrait was done.

"Perfect!" Wendi said. The other Scoop Troopers nodded.

"Places everyone," Christopher said. He motioned for Mark to walk over to the camera and set the auto timer to take a picture.

Then Mark ran to his place as Wendi held the picture of a smiling Mr. Naynum. *Why wait for hope,* Wendi thought, *when you can spread it?*

SCOOP TROOP ALERT

Take a look at hope as it exists in the Bible and in your walk with God. What are some examples of God, Jesus, or people of faith bringing hope to others in the Bible? Do you have a personal favorite, and if so, why?

How have certain people or events brought hope to your life? List some examples and choose one to go into further detail with.

How do you see yourself bringing hope into the lives of others: past, present, and future?

Finding that Healing Feeling

● ● ● ● ● ● ● ● ● ● ● ● ● ●

> *What does God do when bad things happen?*
> **God heals.**

Mark didn't want to admit it, but the news about Mr. Naynum's mom really shook him up, and for two reasons: First of all, he didn't like to hear that anyone close to him was struggling with any type of sickness, either personally or in their family. And second, hearing about illness made Mark obsess about it. He couldn't get it off his mind. It was one thing to look like the King of All Jokes to the rest of the Scoop Troop (even if they didn't laugh half the time), but to be hog-tied in a knot of worry? Ugh. What's more, Mark felt doubly guilty. If someone else was suffering and in the hospital, why was he being so self-centered and turning it into his own little drama?

Most people have a nervous habit. Some people smoke. Others bite their nails. Christopher could be a big-time pacer after a double-tall mocha latte. Rob became a blabbermouth when he got worked up. And Wendi, Mark knew, would scratch her scalp until dandruff snowed down on her shoulders. Yet for all the teasing Mark aimed at Wendi, he never once razzed her for that—because he had a shameful secret.

When Mark felt pressured or under stress, he talked to himself. It wasn't the same as praying out loud to God. Nor were these hushed little comments under his breath. No, Mark Engstrom would talk to Mark Engstrom as if there were another person sitting in the room. His parents had caught him doing it a couple of times at home and at first didn't think much of it. But the most recent time, they had actually mentioned taking him to see a psychologist. Mark didn't know if it was a joke or an idle threat. But it certainly didn't help with his shame.

The church basement, post-Scoop Troop photo shoot, was empty except for Mark. And Mark had a lot on his mind. So he began to jabber.

"This illness thing," Mark said. "It just doesn't make sense to me. Can't for the life of me figure out why people have to suffer, especially the good people. ARGH! It just upsets me! I shouldn't even be thinking about this. And I'm, like, not even a teenager? But I..."

"Yo! Mark! Who are you talking to?" It was Monica.

Gulp! In that split second, thoughts scurried through Mark's mind like cockroaches. He wanted to pick up his books and run. Maybe he could convince his parents to move the family to another state. He'd tell Monica that he was rehearsing for the school play (even though he'd never acted before in his life). He felt faint. Would Monica take a bribe? *Uhmmm. Errr.* "Snagged," he managed to gasp, his face turning cherry red.

"What are you talking about?" Monica asked. Her expression registered genuine surprise as opposed to a sense of "gotcha!"

"Monica!" Mark said. "You and I both know that you just caught me having a very loud conversation with myself."

"Actually," Monica said, "I didn't know that until you just told me."

Mark gulped again.

"So I guess this means you're going to tell everyone," Mark said. "And when everyone finds out—especially Wendi—they'll kick me out of the Scoop Troop faster than you can say 'Mark's jokes rock.'"

Monica patted Mark on the back and smiled. "Sit down," she said. "Let's have a chat here, sinner to sinner. So you talk to yourself. What's the big deal? I know lots of people who do that."

"Yeah, but how many kids have parents who are ready to take them to the shrink over it?" Mark replied.

"So you want to talk about parents, eh?" Monica said.

"Monica," Mark said. "I appreciate what you're doing. Really, I do. But if anyone in the Scoop Troop has a reason to look down on me, it's you. You don't have any weird habits or anything. From what I can see, you're pretty much a perfect person, or as close as it gets."

"And that, Mark Engstrom, is my big downfall," Monica said.

"Yeah. Right. Being perfect. I feel *sooo* sorry for you."

"No, Mark, being a *perfectionist*. I'm a perfectionist. And it really is horrible. You have no idea."

Mark could see Monica's eyes starting to mist a bit. He decided to listen rather than talk back.

"Mark, I've got a dad who's a doctor and a mom who's a professor," Monica said. "If I bring home a report card with all A's and one B+, do you know what my mom says? Do you have any idea? She doesn't say, 'Nice going, Monica!' or 'Look at all those A's!' No, she grills me: 'And why did you get this B+? Was there something you could've done better? Do you have any idea how competitive the Ivy League schools are?' And so I push myself. I push myself, hoping that if I do that much better, I can impress her or win her approval. Or that my dad, who's off in his own world, will stop to call and say, 'Monica, I'm so proud of you.'"

Mark said nothing.

"Look, Mark, I'm sorry," Monica said, trying to regain her composure. "Maybe I have some steam to blow off myself. I didn't mean to make this about me and not about you."

"That's funny," Mark said. "A big reason I was talking to myself is that I'm upset over the news about Mr. Naynum's mom, and how I've turned it into my own little obsession. All about *me*, you might say."

Monica chuckled. "I'm definitely not laughing about the situation with Mr. Naynum. It's just funny to me that we've *all* been worried, yet we're just not talking to each other. Here's the thing. Everything about this just reminds me how we're not alone. We're not meant to be alone. And that God heals."

"Preach on, Sister Monica," Mark said, smiling.

SCOOP TROOP ALERT

While Monica and Mark talk, discuss ways God can heal. Here are some ideas to get you started:

SALVATION: Through Jesus' death on the cross, the sins of God's people were taken away.

PHYSICAL MIRACLES: In the Bible, Jesus heals lepers and raises Lazarus from the dead.

COMFORT: In the Book of Psalms, messages of suffering and recovery remind us we are not alone.

RESTORATION: Job, who has everything taken from him, is given back his health, fortune, and a new family.

"Isn't it natural that when there's a crisis, people start to worry?" Monica asked. "And when they worry, their worst sides often show? And that the people they're worrying about need healing, too? Some things are too big for us. I can't even straighten out my own life right now. But nothing is impossible to God."

"A God," Mark added, "who knows all about healing."

"Preach on, Brother Mark!" Monica said. She reached over and gave him a big hug. "I am so glad you are my friend."

"Me, too," Mark said.

"Are you sure that wasn't you talking to yourself, Mark?" Monica asked.

"Thanks for pointing out that flaw, Miss Monica the Perfectionist."

They cracked up, just in time for Christopher to enter the room. He'd forgotten his backpack. He stared at the two as they headed out, still laughing. "How come," Christopher said, "I never *ever* know what's going on?"

SCOOP TROOP ALERT

Your assignment for the *Good Newspaper* is to create a prayer of healing for yourself or a loved one. Don't just write it: Give it a title, decorate it, make it a poem, put it down in fancy script or offbeat colors.

Here is an example of a prayer that Mark wrote:

Dear Jesus:

Thank you for always looking out for me. I am coming to you because I have this problem. I know you love me just as I am, but I would like to be helped in this area. I talk to myself when I get stressed out. It's embarrassing because other people sometimes overhear me.

I've been doing it ever since my older brother Chuck got sick two years ago and almost died. I know he's better now, thanks to you. But I still worry whenever I hear someone close to me is sick. Help me to deal with this, and thanks. Your will be done! Amen.

Mark Engstrom

Good Morning, God Mourning

• • • • • • • • • • • •

> *What does God do
> when bad things happen?*
> **God mourns.**

On Thursday morning, the Scoop Troopers found this e-mail message when checking the in-boxes of their home computers. It was from Mr. Naynum:

Dear Scoop Troopers:

After 66 years on this planet, my mother passed away Tuesday evening in her sleep. I take comfort knowing she is now with the God she loved so much.

I wanted to write this letter to all of you because I won't be around for the next two weeks as my family and I prepare for the funeral and private mourning time. I trust that the *Good Newspaper*, true to its name, is in good hands. I've often wondered why times like these cause some people to draw closer to God and others to doubt or even deny his existence. Believe it or not, you've helped me to get some clarity on this.

About a month ago, when we were chatting in a news meeting, Mark brought up a song called "Dear God," by XTC.

I had to confess that I'd never heard of the song or the group before. But when Mark shared the lyrics with us, I was shocked. If you'll recall, the song takes the form of a letter to God, with the singer sharing all the reasons he refuses to believe that there is a God. Two lines stuck out in my head:

> *You're always letting us humans down*
> *The wars you bring, the babes you drown.*

That touches on some age-old questions, doesn't it? If God really does exist, and if God is loving, how can God allow so much suffering to go on in the world? And why do good people die?

Momma told me a story when I was a kid about an angel who didn't like the way God ran things. He started grumbling, so one day God said, "I'll tell you what: You seem so sure you can do a better job at running the universe, I'll let you take over for a while." So God took a rest, and the angel set right to work making things the way he thought they ought to be.

The first thing that angel did was stop death, because he was tired of watching the human race suffer. And the humans were overjoyed at first. Meanwhile, the crops in the fields kept growing and growing and growing; everywhere it was life, life, life and no death.

But then things started to take a nasty turn. The old and diseased people who were in pain and waiting to go were forced to hang on past their time, like leaves unable to fall off a tree. And the new vegetables and fruits had a funny, bland taste to them. Seems that without the compost to feed them—the stuff of death—there was nothing to properly nourish the life. People started to go hungry. There was more suffering after the angel's meddling than there was in the first place. Though I don't understand it, Troopers, death is a part of life. And what's more, I'm convinced that every time a brave soldier or innocent civilian falls, or a baby drowns, God is right there mourning. If God intervened at every step of our lives, and saved us from every last hurt, we would not be free human beings made in God's image. We'd be puppets.

What God *did* free us from is sin. And to do that, God became a human and went to the cross himself, experiencing the most humiliating, painful death imaginable so that he could identify with all of our trials. Even before that, Jesus showed us his compassion when he saw his dead friend Lazarus and wept. Then he raised him.

I'm confident Jesus has done the same with my mother's soul. And I also believe that he's joining me in my mourning. It's hard to describe the loss I feel, even though she's been ill for some time. Still, I'm humbled because his presence is impossible to ignore. He's giving me strength even in my weakness.

Please, don't worry about me. Pray instead. I'll see you soon.

In God's Peace,

Mr. Naynum

SCOOP TROOP ALERT

In the Beatitudes (Matthew 5:1-12), Jesus said, "Blessed are those who mourn, for they shall be comforted." What are some ways to comfort someone who is mourning? Think beyond flowers or responses such as, "I am so sorry." Some people, for example, deliver home-cooked meals to the bereaved. Often, the best gestures don't require words.

If you were to see Mr. Naynum on his return to Shorewood Park Church, what would you do? Think of your own ideas and then discuss them with your group.

A Reason to Live
and a-Raisin' the Dead

• • • • • • • • • • • • • •

> *What does God do*
> *when bad things happen?*
> **God raises from the dead.**

"Okay, Troopers," Christopher said, calling another news meeting to order. "We're going to have to do this one without Wendi."

"Where is she?" Monica asked, figuring the girl had gone off and decided to get a purple Mohawk.

"She had to have one of her three cats put down," Christopher said. "She said it was cat diabetes or something like that."

"Aw!" Monica responded. If there was one passion Monica and Wendi shared—probably the only one—it was a love of animals. Monica used to have a big hairy sheepdog named Milkshake. She loved that shaggy pooch and was sad to see him pass away, even though 16 years is an awfully long time for a dog to live. He died three years ago and it still seemed like it happened yesterday.

"Does anyone know how's she's doing?" Monica asked.

"Well, based on what Christopher just said, I think the cat is dead," Mark replied with a smirk.

"Mark!" Monica snapped. "Please. This is no time for jokes, especially yours. How is WENDI is what I meant."

"I gathered," Christopher said. "You know, she seems to be taking it pretty well, considering. The cat was old and had been sick for a long time. Wendi was starting to get worn down by all the trips to the vet and didn't want to see her suffer any longer."

"Okay, just to preface, I'm not being funny here," Mark said. "But did you ever wonder what happens to animals when they die? Where do their souls end up? Do pets go up to heaven to wait for their masters? And if they've been really good do they get a shot at becoming human? Or what if they've been really bad? Does the devil have any use for bad animals?"

"I don't think the devil has any use for anything," Christopher said, "unless you count burning up souls the way a rocket engine uses fuel. Souls go down and the flames rise up."

"Speaking of rising," Monica said, "I've always wondered about Jesus raising Lazarus from the dead. There he is, the Son of God, and he's about to do something utterly impossible for any human being to do."

"This much we know," Mark interjected.

"But that's not what puzzles me," Monica said. "If he's going to do something that fantastic, then why does Jesus say, 'Roll away the stone' from the grave? Couldn't he have just waved his hand and made the stone sail through the air like a ping-pong ball? That would've wowed everyone."

"Maybe he wanted to see how strong the faith of the people was," Rob offered. "It's like, 'If you want a miracle, then show me you believe it can actually happen. Take the first step.'"

"For a guy who doesn't talk much, Rob, you don't waste a word," Monica said.

"Funny you should say that, though," he replied. "Sometimes I feel like the stone is in front of my own heart."

"What do you mean?" asked Christopher, looking puzzled.

"Jesus says, 'I stand at the door and knock' when he talks about entering our hearts. And for me, that's just like what I imagine when I see him standing in front of Lazarus's tomb.

Only it's my heart that's in there. Sometimes I feel like I'm dead to love."

Monica gasped to herself, not just for Rob's confession, but because suddenly the quiet one was off and running at the mouth again.

"Dead to love," Rob continued, "dead to caring about anyone and anything but me and whatever my needs are at the current moment. And worst of all, I'm dead to believing that Jesus really raised himself from the dead, because it all seems just too incredible a story."

"Now there's a deadly sin," Mark said.

"I can believe so many other things that happened in the Bible without batting an eye," Rob said. "Lepers being cleansed. Lame people walking. Water being turned to wine. Even Jesus being born of a virgin. But why is it that I have a problem with the Lazarus story? Or that I can't figure out the resurrection for that matter?"

It was as if Rob had asked for a minute of silence in honor of Wendi's cat.

"Hey, Rob," Monica said. "Quick question: Isn't your middle name Thomas?"

"No, it's Kevin. Why?"

"Well, it should be Thomas—as in *doubting* Thomas."

"What are you talking about Monica?" said Rob, who sounded a touch flustered.

"I'm not saying there's anything wrong with you," Monica said. "But it's obvious that you'd like a sign. Proof. A wounded side to stick your hand into. A DVD of the event that you can watch over and over and over. On the one hand, you're asking some pretty mature questions. I wish I knew all the answers. But you're forgetting one thing: Raising a soul from the dead is not a human ability. It's God's. We'll never fully comprehend it. You have to take a leap of faith!"

"And besides," Christopher said, "maybe all the proof you need is right in front of you."

"But miracles like that don't happen today," Rob said.

"They do, Rob, if you know where to look," Christopher responded. "You're an artist. Your whole life is about seeing things from a different angle. Well, I've seen the dead rise. I've seen people who were spiritually dead reborn after they came to know Jesus. You see them, and it's like encountering a whole new person. I've seen people who should've been crushed by tragedies rise up with incredible strength."

"Ahhh," Rob said, the light bulb flickering on in his head.

"Take Mr. Naynum," Christopher said. "He just lost his mother, the woman he loves more than anyone in this world except for his wife. And I can guarantee you that thanks to God, he'll be back here soon, rising from the ashes of his grief."

"Ohhh, Christopher, that's so poetic!" Monica gushed. The lilt in her voice turned him into beet-red mush.

"No, it's only poetic if he rhymes *grief* with *thief* or *relief*," Mark said.

"As if you have a better way of putting it, Mark," Monica said.

"How about this?" Mark asked. "I think God needs a business motto for skeptics like Rob. 'Jesus: A Reason to Live and a-Raisin' the Dead.'"

"Oh, brother," Monica said, shaking her head.

"That's *Brother Mark* to you," he said. "Now if you don't mind, pass the collection plate up with a hefty contribution, please."

"As long as I can wrap it in this used wad of gum," Monica said. She pulled it out of her mouth, walked up to Mark, and pressed it on his nose.

SCOOP TROOP ALERT

In addition to raising the dead, God has the power to raise us out of trouble. God restores us, gives us strength, and washes away our sins.

For this exercise, recall a time in your life when you felt "raised up" by God—that is, pulled out of a depressing, uncertain situation or stuck circumstance. What changed over time? How did God make his presence known to you? How were your prayers answered—or answered differently than you expected? And finally, how did the experience change your faith?

My Cup Bowleth Over

> *What does God do*
> *when bad things happen?*
> **God comforts.**

"Do you think it's a good idea to hold a Scoop Troop meeting here?" Monica asked Christopher. "In a bowling alley?"

Monica hoped that someday Christopher might notice her as more than just another member of the Troop. She'd worn brand new black jeans and a beautiful white angora sweater her mother had given her for Christmas. But boys never seem to pick up on those things, do they? Sigh.

Christopher, in fact, couldn't notice anything about Monica at the moment. He was crouched on the floor of the 7-10 Lanes, right in front of the shoe rental counter, trying to squeeze into a hideous pair of green-and-purple bowling shoes.

"Look, Monica," Christopher said. "You've got flashing lights, video screens, cheese fries, pool tables, and rubber bumpers so that there are never, ever any gutter balls. What's not to like?"

"Besides," Wendi said, "this is the one thing Mr. Naynum loves to do that's silly. If anything can help him get back on his feet, this will."

"Not that I'd count on getting anything done for the next issue of the *Good Newspaper*," said Monica, a bit annoyed. (Maybe it was more because Christopher wasn't paying much attention to her.) "I know, I know. Helping Mr. Naynum is important. But sometimes I feel like I'm the only one who's thinking up any good ideas."

"Sheesh," said Mark. "And what was wrong with my latest suggestion?"

"Mark, you didn't really think we were going to do a feature on torture devices used in the Bible?" Monica asked. "Or did you?"

"Forget it," Mark replied. "Just forget it. Forget that I…"

And there he was, entering the bowling alley like … like … well, not exactly like a cowboy or a superhero, or even someone who could roll a 100 game. Still, he had a certain swagger to him, dressed in flair-leg polyester pants with a red-and-black plaid pattern, matching plaid shoes *(huh?)*, and a bowling shirt. And oh, what a shirt: a purple silk short-sleeve number with gold piping and the name "RALPH" emblazoned in cursive writing. In his left hand he carried a spotless white-leather ball bag.

"Ralph?" Wendi asked. "Who's RALPH?"

"It can't be Mr. Naynum," Mark said.

"I thought his first name was 'George,'" Christopher said.

"And so it is, my friend!" Mr. Naynum exclaimed as he bounded over to the scoring table outside lanes 11 and 12. You would've thought he'd just returned from the Pro Bowlers Tour, the way the Scoop Troopers crowded around and embraced him.

Mr. Naynum laughed. "So I guess you wanna know why it says, 'RALPH,' on my shirt," Mr. Naynum said.

"Actually, I want to know where you got the cool pants," Mark said.

"Sorry, Mark, they won't help make your jokes any better," Wendi said. "Though they might make you look like a joke."

Mark made a loud whistling sound that dipped in pitch. "Hear that, Wendi? That's the sound of you, going down as I crush you frame after frame! Though you could just give up now, while the score is still tied."

"But we haven't even started yet," Wendi said, a bit confused.

"Precisely!" Mark responded.

"I can see not much has changed since I've been away," Mr. Naynum said, shaking his head.

"So you never told us why you have a different name on your shirt," Christopher said. "Did it used to belong to someone in your family?"

"Or maybe you won it in a bowl-off," offered Rob.

"First name of your bowling hero?" Mark asked.

"To all of those fine guesses, the answer is no," Mr. Naynum said. "You see, Ralph is my bowling name."

"Your what?" Rob asked.

"My bowling name! I bought this shirt at a thrift shop, which means it used to belong to someone else who I assume was named Ralph—unless the last owner used it as his bowling name, too. So anyway, Ralph is my bowling name. Kind of like an alley alias."

"Or a stage name," Christopher added.

"Exactly," Mr. Naynum said.

"So should we call you Ralph?" Wendi asked.

"Only if you have your own bowling names," Mr. Naynum responded. "But make 'em good. Something with a bit of flair."

"I want to be Darla," Wendi said.

"I'm Eggbert," Rob chipped in.

Mark said, "Call me Angus."

Christopher said, "Carlo here. Ciao, baby."

Monica said, "I'll *beeeee*… Penelope!"

"All right!" Mr. Naynum said. "Now everyone go pick out a ball."

"Can we see your bowling ball, Mr. Naynum?" Monica asked.

"You mean 'Ralph', Monica," Mark corrected.

"You mean 'Penelope', Angus," Monica responded.

"Nice," Mark said.

Mr. Naynum unzipped his bag and pulled out a 14-pound ball polished to perfection. And what a strange ball it was: yellow as a banana, emblazoned with "Ralph" in cursive script.

"Wow!" Christopher said.

"I can't believe you got a ball with your bowling name on it," Mark said.

"A gift from Mom," Mr. Naynum said. And though the Troopers looked for signs of tears, or choking up, there weren't any. Mr. Naynum just smiled, sublime enough to suggest he was at peace.

"Can I say something, since you all look like you're worried about me?" Mr. Naynum asked. "I cannot describe the amount of comfort I've felt over the last two weeks. I've been surrounded by family, including a lot of relatives I haven't seen in years. My wife and kids have been great. Friends dropped by almost every night with food and words of encouragement. And that picture you all sent over to me—with the banner that Rob drew with the word 'HOPE' on it? I can't tell you how well timed that was. I was having a really bad afternoon when that came in the mail. It picked my spirits up like *that*." He snapped his fingers.

Rob blushed and tilted his head down to obscure his sheepish grin.

"Troopers, it's true. God brings comfort," Mr. Naynum said. "That doesn't mean I'm done mourning, or that I'll ever stop missing my mother. But life has to go on. And this is the perfect way for me to get back into the game."

"The bowling game!" Christopher said.

And in that moment, though no one noticed, Monica felt ashamed. This gathering wasn't about her or her clothes. It wasn't about impressing a boy. And it wasn't about trying to crank out ideas for another *Good Newspaper*. It was all about comforting a near and dear mentor.

"Excuse me for a second, guys," Monica said. "I'll be right back." She ran off to the bathroom and locked herself in a stall. And she began to cry.

What seemed like a minute later, she heard a familiar voice say, "Monica?"

Oh great, Monica thought. *It's Wendi.*

Monica tried to gather her composure in an instant and look unruffled. You get plenty of practice when you have a mom who's a demanding perfectionist. She stepped out of the stall.

"I'm just fine!" Monica said, grinning like she was resisting a stiff wind.

Wendi wrinkled her eyebrow and looked at Monica skeptically. "No you're not. You've been in here 15 minutes."

That long? Monica thought. *Oh, no.*

"But you know what? We'll talk about it later. Or maybe not. It's not really any of my business," Wendi said.

And then Wendi did something extraordinary.

She reached over and gave Monica a hug. Stiff and brief, to be sure. But it was a hug. And from Wendi Best, of all people.

As Wendi walked away, she yelled back to Monica, "Come bowl with us! Or else I'll send Mark in after you!"

Monica giggled at the image. Now that would be truly uncomfortable. But as for what had just happened, Monica decided that Mr. Naynum was right. God gives comfort—and often, as she just witnessed, in the most unexpected ways.

SCOOP TROOP ALERT

Just as God comforts us, we have the ability to comfort others. One way is to LISTEN. You don't always have to have answers. Listening can be enough. When you are listening to someone, try using the 80-20 rule: LISTEN 80 percent of the time and TALK 20 percent of the time. When you do talk, avoid giving advice or passing judgment. Try to understand what the person is feeling.

Think about the bowling alley scene. Imagine that you are the one that catches Monica in her moment of tears. (If you're a boy, assume it takes place at the snack bar and not the girls' bathroom, okay?) How would you handle the situation? What did you think of the way Wendi treated Monica? Could she, for example, have spent more time with her? Was she a good listener?

The Scoop Troopers have asked you to sign a card for Mr. Naynum. But they just don't want you to sign it: They've picked you to say something that will speak comfort on behalf of the whole group! Oh no! What would you say and why?

Disciple

Here's the Scoop
on the Scoop Troop

• • • • • • • • • • • •

> *Why do I tell others about God?*
> **Because it's part of being
> a Christian.**

Ever since five students at Shorewood Park Church banded together to form the *Good Newspaper*, they've gotten lots of attention from readers who want to know more about them. So in their latest issue, the Scoop Troopers have decided to write little profiles about themselves. Here's what they had to say:

Name: Christopher Lewis

Hobbies and interests: Playing guitar and song writing, reading books about the 1960s, hiking, keeping a journal.

Position: I'm the editor of the *Good Newspaper* because everyone says it was my idea, even though I have no clue what they're talking about. I blurted out something at a youth group meeting about trying to get the "good news" out, and here I am.

My favorite way to tell others about God: Even though I love writing for the newspaper, I love writing songs more. A song is powerful enough to touch people in ways that other forms of expression can't. I don't like to preach at people. I just try to show them what an amazing world God has made, and how I see things through the eyes of a Christian.

Name: Mark Engstrom

Hobbies and interests: I play solitaire a lot. I'm into video games. I've read all the Harry Potter books and the Chronicles of Narnia. But none of that matters until you get to know me and find out just how hysterical I truly am.

Position: Reporter, but I'm working on a humor column too. I was inspired by reading this really funny book called *The Lutheran Handbook* and came up with my own ideas for some lists, like "Ten Risk-Free Miracles Novices Can Try" and "Five Things the Hell-Bound Can Expect Once They Arrive in the Fiery Pit." Please tell the staff you'd read something like that, okay?

My favorite way to tell others about God: Sometimes I go to the senior center and tell "God jokes" to the people there. Seriously. It feels good to hear them laughing at me. Wendi says they're laughing at me but for a different reason.

Name: Wendi Best

Hobbies and interests: I have a greyhound named Ethel that I got from animal rescue. She used to be a racing dog. I also have three cats. I like searching thrift shops for cool clothes. I also love to watch talk shows. Oh, and dying my hair pink.

Position: I'm a reporter for the paper, but during staff meetings I also like to be the reality-check person. Mostly, this involves keeping Mark Engstrom from cracking too many of his dumb jokes.

My favorite way to tell others about God: This newspaper has been great for me, because every time I get depressed about my own life, I take that energy and channel it into work for the next issue. I love to write, and it inspires me that the Bible is a book of timeless writings. Someday I'd like to publish a book that gives people a reason to keep going, especially during the times life seems like crap. (Can I say the word *crap* in this essay, Christopher?)

Name: Monica Perez

Hobbies and interests: I love nice clothes! I'm also into puzzles and games and incredible bizarre bargains at garage sales. That's where I found Mainframe, my $20 talking computer that sounds just like the movie star Donny Sheek.

Position: I'm working on my own advice column, and I love to come up with ideas at staff meetings. Lots of ideas.

My favorite way to tell others about God: Besides the *Good Newspaper*? I have a Web site that has my journal on it. Though I was raised in a Christian family, I remember making a full commitment to my faith just about two years ago. Since then, I have kept a blog that details my everyday struggles and victories, joys and concerns. I've gotten a few hundred hits over the last couple months, and some people have written really nice things about how I've inspired them.

Name: Rob Jordan

Hobbies and interests: Drawing. That and delving into mysteries and dilemmas that are mostly impossible to figure out.

Position: I'm the illustrator for the *Good Newspaper*. I don't talk all that much, except when I get caught up in mysteries and dilemmas that are mostly impossible to figure out.

My favorite way to tell others about God: I would say drawing pictures. Because a picture paints 1,000 words, right? But my problem is that I have a real problem sharing my faith with anyone. I know Jesus is important to me and all, but who wants to be preached at? And how do I know that they'd take anything I say seriously? Or maybe they would just wait until I leave and laugh at me and call me one of those crazy Christian people. So I don't say anything. But

I should. And it makes me feel guilty. And I… *(Editor's Note: We've edited out the rest of Rob's reply because we figured you got the point by now.)*

Name: Mr. George Naynum

Hobbies and interests: Bowling, listening to jazz, gardening, riding my motorcycle on long trips.

Position: Advisor for the *Good Newspaper.*

My favorite way to tell others about God: At first I didn't want to write an essay because the kids are truly the stars of this show. But they insisted, and so here I am. Fittingly they've given me some space to talk not about myself but about God, which is how it should be—though I will share a story from my own life.

I read Rob's essay, and I know exactly how he feels. When I was a young man I hated getting anything shoved down my throat. I even left the church for a while because I was bitter about a lot of things, including growing up without a father. Then I met this kid at my first job in the college dining hall.

His name was Anthony Urbanski, and he was one of the most amazing people I'd ever met. He worked twice as hard as anyone—always the first to arrive and the last to leave. If he got assigned some horrible job, he never complained about it. He never had a bad word to say about anyone, which was tough since everyone used to gossip, including me. I used to love just being around him, and I know a lot of other people felt the same way.

One day I was feeling down and asked him point blank: "Anthony, how do you do it? How do you stay so together and so positive when everyone around you is just hanging on?"

Anthony said two things I'll never forget. First: "Oh, I don't think I'm any different from any other student who works here. I've got my problems, too. But every day, I get all the help I need." And second: "George, do you mind if I tell you about my best friend?" And that best friend turned out to be Jesus.

I was so overwhelmed by Anthony's example that I decided I wanted to be more like him. I understand now that I was getting a glimpse of the Savior inside him. And when I asked him years later why he shared his testimony with me, he replied, "Simple, George. It's part of being a Christian. If I were a guitar player, I'd play. If I were a teacher, I'd teach. And as a believer, I not only believe, but share my belief with those around me in a humble but assertive way."

So what are my favorite ways to tell people about God? I try to bring excellence to all I do. And when I see an opening to talk with someone who's hurting about all Jesus has done for me, I'm not shy. I share.

SCOOP TROOP ALERT

You're a part of the Scoop Troop team, too! As we begin this Disciple unit, your task is to write your own mini-essay following the same format the Troopers just used. Your position? That's easy: Give yourself your own dream newspaper job. And when it comes to the question about how you share your faith, be honest. If you're high-tech and gung-ho like Monica, say so. But if you're doubtful and have problems like Rob, write about that instead. If you fall into the latter, you may want to make a note of the roadblocks that keep you from sharing your faith.

Wendi Does Obedience School

* * * * * * * * * * * * * * * * *

> *Why do I tell others about God?*
> **Because Jesus calls us to**
> **tell others.**

"Okay, where's Wendi?" Mark asked. "This is an important news meeting, and we can't get it started without her."

"What's so important about it—opposed to any other *Good Newspaper* meeting, I mean?" Christopher asked.

"Oh, I don't know!" Mark replied, grinning. "But I sure sounded take-charge for a moment there, didn't I?"

"If Wendi were here, she'd have the perfect comeback," Monica said. "Like, if you wanna take charge, Mark, just lick your finger. The electric socket's right over there."

Mark scrunched his nose at Monica. "Way to socket to me, Monica. Get it? *Socket* to me!"

Monica decided to change the subject to something Mark couldn't joke about. "Please don't tell me that another one of Wendi's cats died."

"Doubtful," Christopher said. "In fact, she just got a kitten from a neighbor. There's something about the number 3 and Wendi where cats are concerned. I think she might be superstitious."

Just then Wendi stormed in, stomping down the stairs as if she'd been hit in the head by a baseball.

"I didn't mean it," Christopher said sheepishly.

"*Arrrggg!* That Ms. Truxton! I can't stand her!" Wendi said, fuming.

The Scoop Troopers all attended Hinton Heights Middle School, not far from the church. And if there was one teacher who always seemed to have it in for Wendi, Ms. Truxton was it. She was about three years away from retiring, and Wendi had a theory that Ms. Truxton was trying to take out all her venom on certain students before leaving the school. Not that Wendi ever helped matters with her sharp tongue, either.

"I'm standing in line, waiting to get back into the building after the fire drill, right?" Wendi said. "And I'm holding this soggy banana peel in my hand. The banana was from lunch. When the alarm went off, I just took it with me."

"Then you threw it at her," Rob said.

"I wish," Wendi said. "I stepped out of line to throw it out in the dumpster—that's all I did—and Ms. Truxton grabs me by the shoulder: 'You! Best!' she said. 'You just earned yourself a detention.'"

"Sounds like you slipped on that banana peel hard," Mark joked.

"Mark!" Monica shouted. "So what happened next Wendi?"

"So I was in detention and I had to write an essay—and get this—the topic was obedience. 'If a teacher tells you to do something, why is it a good idea to be obedient?'"

"So what did you write?" Christopher asked.

"I said that obedience was super important to me," Wendi replied. "So important that I live by the chain of command, since my dad used to be in the army. That means I obey my parents ahead of everyone else, including my teachers, and my dad taught me not to suffer fools gladly. So, if a teacher decides to be mean and unfair by punishing me for throwing out a lousy banana peel, it would be disrespectful to my parents not to voice a loud, strenuous objection."

"Oh, boy," Christopher said, shaking his head. "Let me guess: double detention."

"Starting tomorrow," Wendi said. "But it was worth it."

Mr. Naynum, who had been silently observing the whole time, spoke up. "May I interject something, Miss Wendi?"

Wendi admired Mr. Naynum very much and was not about to say no. But she could tell by the tone of his voice that she wasn't going to like much of what he had to say.

"Sure," Wendi said, gulping down. "Shoot."

"I agree with you, Ms. Truxton is a bit of a character. I have a lot of friends who teach at Hinton Heights and can't figure out what her deal is. And I have to admit that your essay was brilliant. But you know what?"

"What?" Wendi said.

"That's how wars get started," Mr. Naynum said. "Whether it's your little battle with Ms. Truxton, a couple of street gangs trying to prove who's more macho, or a conflict between nations. Someone fires, and the other party fires back."

Wendi nodded.

"Jesus told us to turn the other cheek," Mr. Naynum added. "And I'll admit, that isn't easy. But if you really want to take that whole notion of 'chain of command' seriously, then Jesus ranks first. He's the God of all. And I think he might be telling you a few things here. A few things for us all, in fact."

"What would that be?" Monica asked. She could feel Wendi squirming and wanted to take some of the heat off of her.

"Troopers, listen up: It's who we are and what we do that speak volumes about what Christ means to us. How he's transformed us. How he makes a difference each and every day. Sure, we're human. I get mad whenever someone cuts me off in traffic. You wouldn't want to hear the words I use sometimes!"

Wendi laughed at that.

"But when we're in front of others, our actions tell them a

lot about how strong we are with God. And we have to do our best to be merciful, loving, forgiving, and tolerant—even when the folks we're dealing with don't deserve it. And why? Because Jesus told us to!"

"I can see how that works even with the *Good Newspaper*," Christopher said. "Maybe I'm the editor, and you're the advisor, Mr. Naynum. But above you and everyone else is Jesus, and he's the reason we're here. If we do anything positive, it's not because we have personal goals. It's not because you told us or the pastor told us. It's because Jesus told us to spread the good news."

"So what should I do?" asked Wendi, who wasn't exactly admitting she was wrong—but wasn't arguing she'd done right, either.

"I'd pray about it," Mr. Naynum said. "Ask God for guidance. Listen to that still small voice. And maybe you can look at some way to make amends to Ms. Truxton." Wendi rolled her eyes.

"Would it help," he asked, "if I told you that her husband passed away two years ago? And that the two of them were planning on retiring in New Mexico? Or that she has three cats, too?"

Wendi drew a deep breath and exhaled, her sigh expressing a mix of regret and resistance. Sure, she had a bit more sympathy for Ms. Truxton after hearing all that. But letting go of her anger and forgiving that mean, miserable woman was going to prove awfully hard. At least that's how she felt.

"Maybe we can pray with you," Mark offered.

"No thanks," Wendi said, picking up her book bag and throwing it on her shoulder. "I've got a lot to think about." And she walked out.

"So now what?" Christopher asked.

"Let's get in a circle," Mark replied. The Troopers huddled in and closed their eyes. And Mark began: "Dear Lord, we thank you for your many blessings and come to you today to pray for our friend Wendi…"

SCOOP TROOP ALERT

Jesus tells us many amazing things in the Bible. But there is also one thing he asks us to do on his behalf: Tell others about God. Why is this important? Here are some reasons to consider:

- Jesus is your FRIEND: You go to Jesus with prayer requests all the time. He will address your needs. If he asks something of you, doesn't it seem right to honor his request?

- Jesus is your PROTECTOR: Jesus will offer you help during all of life's difficulties. But think of all the suffering people in this world who don't have a relationship with Jesus. If you don't tell them, how will they come to know the same security and strength you do?

- Jesus is your SAVIOR: Jesus saved all of us by dying on the cross. He demands nothing of you in return other than your faith. Doesn't experiencing such love make you want to share the good news?

Jesus has told you to go out and spread the gospel. Write him back! Tell him how you feel about this, what you plan to do, what your dreams are as a believer. Tell him anything and everything, because he'll understand. As long as it reflects the nature of your relationship with him, anything works.

Good News Travels Fast

• • • • • • • • • • • • • •

> *Why do I tell others about God?*
> **So others can hear the**
> **good news.**

"Do you ever ask why we are here?" Monica asked the other Scoop Troopers, except for Wendi, who was finishing her double detention at Hinton Heights Middle School. "I mean, really. We didn't know each other all that well before we started doing this *Good Newspaper* for the church. Yet we're sticking it out. And we've become close friends. So why are we here?"

"Philosophically speaking," Mark began, "the question 'Why are we here?' is as old as time itself and requires an answer of supernatural intelligence. So allow me to gaze into my crystal ball…"

"And see the reflection of spinach caught in your teeth and a booger hanging from your left nostril," Monica interjected with a grin.

"Har-de-har-har," Mark said, smirking. "Nice one, Monica —or should I call you Wendi?"

"Wendi asked me not to let you get away with anything while she was gone," Monica explained. "Just doing my job, I guess!"

"Okay, before we forget your question," Christopher said, "I have a thought—a simple one. We're here to spread the good news, of course, so that other people can hear it. If people don't hear the good news, how are they going to know it's out there?"

"True," Rob said. "But what if people aren't *listening*?"

"Then make them listen," Monica said.

"Huh?" said Christopher, a bit alarmed.

"Easy," Monica said. "If you yell over a bullhorn at a pep rally, people are going to hear you. If you make posters that are so large and colorful that they can't be ignored, they're going to attract attention. And if you keep repeating the message over and over, it's going to stick in people's ears—like a song you can't get rid of."

"Oh, you mean an earworm!" Rob said.

"A what?" Monica asked.

"An earworm. That's when you get a song stuck in your head and it won't go away. I wonder why that happens."

"There goes Rob," Christopher sighed.

"Seriously, my mom was playing the Barney song—you know, 'I love you, you love me'—for my four-year-old brother because it was the only thing that could get him to calm down at bedtime. And because my bedroom is next to his, I'd hear her play it over and over and over. And when she finally shut off the CD player, I could still hear it playing in my head, as if the music hadn't stopped. As a matter of fact, I kept hearing it for about a week: 'I love you! ... You love me! ... We're a ...'"

"Oh, wonderful," said Monica. "Now it's stuck in *my* head."

"Stop, Rob," Mark said, "before I sic a rabid triceratops on your purple dinosaur."

Rob promptly shut up and pulled out his sketch pad. He started tracing out a cartoon of Mark wedged in the gaping jaws of a pterodactyl.

"Earworms aside," Christopher said, "I'm not so sure I agree with you, Monica."

"What do you mean, Christopher?" Monica felt as if she'd just been rejected to her face but tried her best to hide it.

"You can twist people's arms, but that only works up to a point." Christopher said. "I went with my older brother to roadie for him at Mocha Madness on Saturday night. He was playing some of his best songs. People should've been applauding and filling the tip jar. His voice never sounded better. And you know what? About 90 percent of the folks were staring at their laptops, reading a book, or talking on their cell phones. And whenever the coffee grinder fired up, you couldn't hear him all that well. There was some polite clapping here and there, sure. But nothing like what he deserved. A few people even walked right in front of him to use the bathroom!"

"Sort of like when I tell my jokes," Mark said. "The admiration I deserve from all of you is nothing like what I get."

"Oh, *now* I get it," Monica said. "People ignore the *Good Newspaper* because it's corny, dumb, and has an inflated opinion of itself."

"Monica, when I am a famous comedian," Mark said, "everyone else here will get my autograph free of charge. But you will pay, in more ways than one."

"Either that, or Wendi and I will profit handsomely from the tell-all book we'll write: *Mark Engstrom: The Geeky, Dorky Years, and Why They Never Really Ended!*"

"I knew it! You're a tabloid journalist at heart!" Mark exclaimed.

Just then, Wendi entered the church basement. Her expression reflected neither anger nor vengeful delight. "Where's Mr. Naynum?" she asked.

"Bowling," Rob said.

"Of course," Wendi responded.

"So what happened with the rest of your detention?" Mark asked. "I'll bet Ms. Truxton flew around the room on a janitor's mop and screeched, 'I'll get you, my pretty! And your banana peel too!' "

"Not quite," Wendi said. "In fact, she wasn't even there. Not to supervise me, anyway. But I did have a revelation, you could say."

"Do tell," Monica said.

"Well, today I was asked to write an essay about respect. And so I closed my eyes and tried to gather my thoughts. And I saw Jesus on the cross. His enemies surrounded him, mocking him, spitting on him, and yelling at him. Before I knew it I was writing about how much Jesus loved and respected all of humanity. Not just the people who adored him but also the very ones who drove him to die. I wrote: 'Whenever I think life is unfair, I imagine all the trials Jesus went through, and how he never stopped loving people. He models for me what it means to love my enemies and respect others. And I can't imagine anyone who deserves my respect more.' "

"Whoa," said Christopher. "Powerful stuff."

"I wasn't so sure," Wendi said. "In fact, I thought I'd get in trouble for writing about my faith in, you know, a public school detention. But it just came to me. And as I was leaving, something really strange happened."

"What was that?" Mark said.

"Ms. Truxton stopped in to collect the papers," Wendi said. "She didn't look at me—didn't say a word. Then she walked out. But as I was gathering up my stuff, I thought I heard sobbing coming from the end of the hallway, over by the faculty lounge. I looked down the hall, and I saw her—she was reading one of the essays. And I don't know why, but I have a feeling it was mine."

"You know, God does work in mysterious ways," Mark said.

"Maybe it was your paper," Christopher said. "And maybe it wasn't. Still it took a lot of guts to share the gospel like that. Sooner or later she's gonna read it—and it's going to shine."

The thought of that—and God working through her—made Wendi beam.

SCOOP TROOP ALERT

Without forcing anything down anyone's throat, Wendi found a very creative way to share the good news of God. Here are some tips to help YOU spread the good news:

Be SINCERE: Make sure you speak from your heart. Speaking with passion from your heart will help get your message across.

Be CALM: If you let anger or frustration rule your conversations, people won't listen. Be calm, even if the people you are talking to are making it difficult.

Keep it SIMPLE: Especially for someone who is new to the good news of God, too many details can be overwhelming! Keep your message simple (at least at first). That way, they can hear the good news in words they understand.

Think about someone in your life right now who needs God's love. If you haven't done so already, start praying for them. Find ways to be there for them that will show God's love in action. Speaking of action, write up a plan for sharing the gospel in a sincere, calm, and simple way.

A Mainframe Reframe

Why do I tell others about God?
**So others can understand
the good news.**

"Hey, Monica!" Mark said. "How come you're the only one who knows how to use Mainframe?"

Monica's cheeky computer spoke up first: "My circuits tell me that of all the Scoop Troopers, Monica is by far the most intelligent, the most creative, the most original, the most…"

"Most likely to rescue you from a garbage bin at a garage sale," Wendi interrupted. "I always knew that love is blind. But a computer?"

"Are you saying that I'm *not* all of those things?" Monica asked Wendi. "Intelligent? Creative? Original?"

"It's more the word 'most' that bothers me," Wendi responded. "How do you measure who's the 'most' anything? It's a computer, Monica, not the judge of some popularity contest."

"My circuits are perfectly designed for judging," Mainframe said.

"I'll be the judge of that," Mark offered.

"So, Mark, what do you have against my computer?" Monica asked. She was feeling a bit defensive and tried not to show it, though the irritation colored her voice.

"Nothing at all," Mark responded.

"Yeah, right!" Monica said.

"Monica, for once I get to cut *you* off and you're not even telling a bad joke," Mark said. "Not that I ever tell bad jokes—though you might be…"

"Enough, Mark!" Monica exclaimed. "What's your point?"

"Monica, look at me: my glasses, my khakis, my rugby shirt, my collection of Harry Potter and Narnia books. Now repeat after me: I … am … a … geek."

"Speak for yourself," Monica said. "I'm not a geek."

"No," Mark said. "I'm saying that I am. I, Mark Engstrom, am a geek."

"Whoa, Mark," Christopher said. "Stereotypes aren't nice."

"You don't understand," Mark insisted. "I'm *proud* to be a geek. It's who I am. I don't want to change. And someday, I hope to be a computer geek. But how am I ever going to be a whiz at programming, surfing the Net or building my own Web site until someone shows me how?"

"So why are you looking at me?" Monica asked. She felt nervous, especially since she wasn't used to seeing Mark act this serious. She'd never admit it, but she was hoping he might crack one of his corny jokes just to lighten the mood.

"You have this great computer," Mark said. "Sure, it's strange and all, and it talks like a movie star—but it's cooler than any machine I've ever seen, even my dad's laptop. And I'd *love* to learn how to use it. But how can I—unless you show me how?"

Monica didn't say anything for a moment. She just stared at the ceiling.

"Please tell me that computes," Mark said. "Or have you logged off?"

"Not at all," Monica replied in a subdued voice. "It's just that it reminds me of that story in Acts, the one with Phillip and the Ethiopian. The Ethiopian wanted to know all about Scripture and Jesus but needed someone to help him out."

"Monica," Mark said. "I'm an American of Swedish descent, not an Ethiopian."

"And I'm Monica, not Phillip," she responded. "But the analogy holds up. It's what the *Good Newspaper* is all about. We're here not just to tell people the gospel but help them understand it."

"What's so great about the Bible?" Mainframe complained. "You can't program it like me. You can't print color documents on it like me. You can't send instant messages and..."

"An obvious glitch in the programming," Wendi said.

"Are you sure you still want to learn how to use it?" Rob asked. He dashed off a sketch of Mainframe wrapped in a straightjacket.

"Maybe while I'm learning to use this computer," Mark said, "I could teach it a thing or two."

"Program one dumb joke, and I'll wipe out your hard drive," Monica said to Mark.

"What if I already have?" Mark teased.

"These two microchips are walking down the street," Mainframe said, "and the one says to the other, 'You look circuit bored.' Get it? Bored, meaning 'to lack zest.' And the other says..."

"AAARRRGGGHHH!" Monica yelled.

"Just kidding," Mainframe said.

"Hey, I never laid a finger on it," Mark hastened to add. "Honest."

Monica walked over to her precious computer, rebooted, and turned to face Mark.

"I'll be the judge of that," she said.

SCOOP TROOP ALERT

Make a list of things you want to learn, whether in the near future or at some point in your life. Then stop to consider these questions:

• Who can teach you these things?

• Where would you find these people?

• How might you approach them?

In the case of Phillip and the Ethiopian, Phillip served as a mentor. A mentor is someone who acts as a coach, teacher, or guide, taking a person through the learning and growing process with patience, compassion—and often a good sense of humor. Mentors play an important role in our faith lives. With them at our side, we develop deep bonds of trust, and resilient strength.

Likewise, you can be a mentor too! How can you help lead someone else who's younger than you as they walk with God? Think of a person you can mentor, and describe some ways you can guide them.

Change Is Good, Change Is God

> *Why do I tell others about God?*
> **Because God can change lives.**

The walk from Hinton Heights Middle School to Shorewood Park Church takes about 10 minutes, if you do it alone at a brisk clip and cut across the baseball and soccer practice fields behind the school. But as Monica Perez rushed to catch up with Christopher Lewis—her friend, editor, and secret crush—she hoped that today it might just take a little longer. Or a lot longer.

"Christopher!" Monica called out, breathless from running and the prospect of spending some solo time with her favorite guitar-playing journalist. "Wait up!"

"Sure, Monica," Christopher said, laid back as ever. For his own part, he was perfectly clueless to Monica's feelings—just as he was to most things that weren't plainly spelled out for him. It wasn't that he was dumb. You certainly wouldn't say that if you saw Christopher's test scores.

But most of the time, Christopher's mind was off in some distant place: juggling song ideas, reciting words from his favorite poems and plays, trying to figure out what to eat for a snack. Right now, it was a little mix of the first and the third, as he was quietly goofing around with a lyric about his intense craving for a milkshake:

I'm about to surrender
To putting three scoops in the blender
Pouring in plenty of milk
And blending till it's smooth as silk...

"What are you singing?" Monica asked.

"Oh ... nothing," Christopher said, capping the idea as if shutting off a kitchen faucet.

"Christopher, I have a question. Think I can get your advice?"

"Go for it."

"Do you ever feel sometimes like life isn't going to change?" While Monica appeared to ask this question at face value, there was subtext beneath it—influenced, of course, by Monica's thinly veiled impatience with Christopher. *Why doesn't he notice me?* she thought.

"I feel that way all the time," Christopher said. "Especially when I'm stuck writing a song."

Monica sighed.

"What's the matter?" he asked.

"That's not what I'm talking about at all," Monica said. "This isn't about music. It's about certain people and how *frustrating* they can be."

"Like who?" Christopher asked. He wasn't referring to himself, but his direct eye contact caught Monica off guard. She decided to duck the subject of her attraction to him and share something else that was on her mind.

"Well, take my parents," Monica said. "My dad is so busy being a doctor and spending time with his new wife that I hardly see him at all. I feel like I'm an afterthought in his life. And no matter what I do to remind him that, 'HEY! I'm still around!,' he treats me more like I'm one of his patients than his daughter. And it makes me wonder when he's ever going to come around and realize what he's missing—because I know I'm missing out on things too."

"Interesting," Christopher said.

"So?"

"You're upset because he's basically ignoring you and you'd like to see him change."

"Exactly!" Monica said.

"Do you mind if I tell you a story?" Christopher asked.

"As long as it's not about some girl you like," Monica said, punching his arm.

"What are you talking about?" Christopher asked, looking lost.

"Never mind," Monica said, sighing under her breath. "What's your story?"

"My brother Ben got tickets to that sold-out Anthony Jay show last month. And thanks to a friend, he got into a meet-and-greet after the concert," Christopher said. "It was amazing; the guy played for almost three hours and had two encores. And Ben was really lucky. He not only got an autograph on his T-shirt, but got to talk to Anthony for about 15 minutes—which is forever when you're dealing with a rock star."

"Wow," Monica said. "So what did they talk about?"

"Ben told him about his songs, and Anthony asked for a demo without Ben even having to offer him one. Ben's still excited about that. But the thing Ben wanted to know was what it was like to be famous and headlining a tour. But when he asked Anthony, he didn't start bragging about girls or mansions or big paychecks or guitars or any of that. He just sighed."

"What?"

"He said that being on the road all the time meant being alone, mostly. That he didn't have time for a girlfriend or to see many friends. That he was beginning to lose all of his privacy. That someone always seemed to want something from him. I don't know. Maybe Ben caught the guy at a point where he just needed to vent. But then Anthony said something really strange. He looked right at Ben and asked, 'I wonder what it's going to take for all this to slow down. I never expected this. I'm just 22. When are things going to change?' "

"So what did Ben do?" Monica asked.

"Something really brave, I think. He gave Anthony a big hug and whispered in his ear, 'I'll pray for you, man. God can change lives.' And then he walked away. He said he thought he saw the guy misting up. And Ben won't talk about it, but they've been sending e-mail ever since."

"Christopher, that's amazing," Monica said. "How come you didn't say anything before?"

"Well," Christopher replied, "Ben really wants me to keep it private. Not even my parents know. But you do now."

"It'll be our secret," Monica said, beaming.

"God *can* change lives, Monica," Christopher said. "You can't control what your dad does, but you can control what goes on in your own life. You just have to give up trying to control other people. Everything happens in God's own time."

He squeezed her hand and smiled. "I have to see Mr. Naynum for a minute before the staff meeting," Christopher said before bolting off into the church.

Monica had no clue whether Christopher had a clue! Did he finally figure out that she had feelings for him? *He squeezed my hand!* she thought. *But was it JUST a hand squeeze? Or MORE than just a hand squeeze?* She couldn't tell, but for the time being, it didn't matter. She was on Cloud 11 and a half.

Christopher, meaning 'lover of Christ' in Greek, Monica thought as she stood by the church entrance. *The name fits.*

SCOOP TROOP ALERT

How would you like to change? That's a tough question, so let's look at some things that indicate good change, and some that do not.

- Change is not "instead of": Don't throw out who you are and start over as "someone else." Instead, take an honest inventory of the strengths God has given you, and the areas where you would like to see change.

- Change is teamwork with God: You can do all you can to change, but at a certain point, you must "let go and let God." Trust that God will help you change.

- Change is repentance: No, not guilt, but honest repentance. Look at some of the ways you have been tripped up by sin. Don't worry so much about fixing everything all at once. Instead, ask for God's forgiveness and help to change.

For your assignment, make a plan of change. Keep in mind the descriptions above as you make and carry out your plan. How will this change affect you and those around you?

Church

Love to Worship, Worship to Love

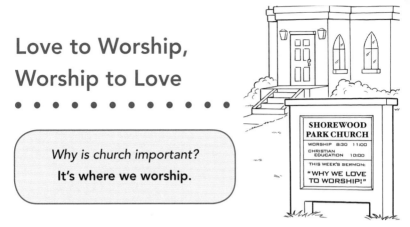

Why is church important?
It's where we worship.

The kids in the **Shorewood Park Church** youth group are using the church basement as a newsroom! The *Good Newspaper* is their way of communicating the gospel message, along with Bible content and history, to kids their age regardless of whether they go to church. This week, the Scoop Troopers have decided to get personal and talk about what worship means to each one of them.

Name: Mainframe, the talking supercomputer

Why I joined the Scoop Troop: Monica Perez bought me at a garage sale for $20, then brought me to the basement of Shorewood Park Church. She uses me for everything from Internet-based research to printing out page designs for the *Good Newspaper.* That's a periodical publication started by the kids in Shorewood Park's youth group to spread the gospel in an informative and engaging way. I came up with the name Scoop Troopers, by the way.

One thing I can do better than anyone else in the Scoop Troop: Calculate the numerical values of pi and the square root of 2 beyond 1,000 digits.

Ambition: To become the first computer to circle the globe in a balloon, unassisted.

What I love best about worship: As a computing device, I cannot worship. This even excludes me from treating my designer as a deity figure. I do, however, experience this phenomenon secondhand through the Scoop Troopers, and I have witnessed many occasions when worship has helped restore a mood of calm and cooperation among the staff. That's a relief. You try having your keys mashed by an upset Scoop Trooper!

Name: Monica Perez

Why I joined the Scoop Troop: To put my skills as an idea person, advice columnist, and all-around good egg to use!

One thing I can do better than anyone else in the Scoop Troop: Bargain shop for clothes. This cashmere sweater I'm wearing? It was on sale for 50 percent off the original $200 price tag and then put on clearance sale for an additional 40 percent off that price. So I wound up paying only $60! It took a month's worth of babysitting gigs to pay for it—but it was worth changing all those diapers. (Yuck.)

Ambition: To become a professional advice columnist, biochemist, and fashion designer. Notice how I did not say *or*. I figure I'll tackle one thing at a time.

What I love best about worship: I usually hate to slow down. I like to work on six things at once, as you might've guessed. I'm the latest in a long line of overachievers. But when I'm in worship, I really enjoy the moments of silence and quiet. It's refreshing to get away from the rushed pace of my life, kind of like floating on a lake after all the splashing has died down. It's one of the few times I'm actually still enough to hear God's voice.

Name: Christopher Lewis

Why I joined the Scoop Troop: That's a toughie, sort of. Everyone insists the *Good Newspaper* was my idea, even though all I did was make a quick comment about "spreading the good news" at a youth group meeting. Next thing I know, I'm the editor of this thing. I never know what's going on. But I really enjoy the company of the other Troopers and the challenge of finding new ways to get "the word" out.

One thing I can do better than anyone else in the Scoop Troop: Play a guitar behind my back. My older brother Ben taught me how to do it, and he taught himself so that he could impress girls. But so far it's not working—for either of us. In fact, the last time I tried it, a girl walked by me and couldn't stop laughing. "That's *soooooooo* 1980s!" she said.

Ambition: I'd just love to put out an album someday. If lots of people buy it, great. But it would be enough just to get the chance to pursue my musical dreams.

What I love best about worship: I don't want to sound corny, but I'm a pretty happy person and have lots to be thankful for. My mom and dad are two of the best parents a kid could ask for; they listen to me and support me in everything.

And when Ben found out I wanted to learn the guitar, he decided to teach me himself. "No one's gonna teach my kid brother the wrong way," he said.

My family makes me feel really special, and I love to thank God in worship because I'm grateful. A lot of kids my age don't have it so good, with divorces, fighting, and worse. It just feels great to thank and praise God. I hope it means something to God, too.

Name: Rob Jordan

Why I joined the Scoop Troop: I love to draw, and in the *Good Newspaper* I get plenty of chances to practice.

One thing I can do better than anyone else in the Scoop Troop: Keep quiet. It's what I'm known for. Except when I'm confronted head-on by one of life's mysteries. Then I run off at the mouth better than anyone else!

Ambition: Graphic designer. And I definitely don't want to run a fast food restaurant. Last summer my brother worked at Hamburger Jester, and every day he'd come home smelling like a giant french fry smothered in ketchup. It drove my beagle nuts.

What I love best about worship: Prayer. When I start a sketch I never know how it will end up. Somewhere along the way, something inside me changes, and it's like an invisible hand guides me. Prayer is like that. I turn all of my uncertainties over to Jesus. I don't know how things will work out. But they always seem to. I can't explain it. But I could try. Do you have 40 minutes?

Name: Mark Engstrom

Why I joined the Scoop Troop: I was abducted by pickle-shaped aliens, blindfolded, and rushed to this place—where the kids were in desperate need of rescue from someone with a tremendous sense of humor.

One thing I can do better than anyone else in the Scoop Troop: Ignore Wendi Best, one of the other Scoop Troopers. Wendi always has something rotten to say about my jokes. Kinda sad to see how jealousy rears its ugly head, don't ya think?

Ambition: Stand-up comic. Will joke for food! But I'd never be a circus clown. Those guys really do scare me. Honest.

What I love best about worship: The joking I do helps me forget about my fears and worries, but not always. When I get really nervous, I talk to myself and it's really embarrassing. But when I'm in church, I love to hear the choir sing. I love the passing of the peace. God really loves me! Me, with all of my faults and problems. That's amazing. Then again, so is Jesus.

Name: Wendi Best

Why I joined the Scoop Troop: Writing in a newspaper is good practice for being a professional writer, and keeping Mark Engstrom in line is good practice for being a parent.

One thing I can do better than anyone else in the Scoop Troop: Monica is the best shopper, but I am definitely the best thrift-shopper. If you buy torn jeans or T-shirts of 1970s bands new off the rack, what fun is that? A few years from now, I hope to be able to add best at bungee jumping too. Right now, my parents won't let me go. Rats.

Ambition: Author and/or a talk-show host. And if I had a magazine named after me, I'd share the cover with my greyhound Ethel every once in a while.

What I love best about worship: Without boring you with all the details, my home life is pretty nuts. Sometimes I wonder why my parents are still together, since they yell at each other all the time. When I go to church on Sundays, it's by myself. I know people call church buildings "sanctuaries," but for me that word has a very real double meaning. When I worship,

I am safe. Nothing or no one can harm me or hurt my feelings. God is close by. I have other people I can spend time with; I like to think of the people at church as my extended family.

Name: Mr. George Naynum

Why I joined the Scoop Troop: As the advisor, I'm technically not a Scoop Trooper. But if you ask me why I'm here, it's because I love kids—and this is one of the most amazing group of kids I've ever met. They're funny, creative, smart, and have great hearts for God.

One thing I can do better than anyone else in the Scoop Troop: Dress up for a bowling match. The next time you see someone with matching plaid pants and bowling shoes, you let me know, because my set is the only one I've ever seen.

Ambition: To live life to its fullest every day and honor God in everything I do. I'll be working on that one for a long, long time!

What I love best about worship: There is nothing—nothing at all—like the experience of gathering with other people to be in God's presence. My "alone time" with God is special, but it's impossible to conceive what my faith walk would be if I didn't have others to worship with. Sharing sorrow and song, brokenness and boisterous celebration, we enter into something much larger than ourselves. And there's nothing I love more than leaving my work week at the door and entering into sabbath. Everyone needs time off from their cares! Plus, I love potlucks. There's never enough time to try out all of the desserts.

SCOOP TROOP ALERT

What do YOU love most about worship? Now is the time to put your thoughts down! Once you've done that, go a step further and design your ideal worship service. What would you include in it? Poetry? What kind of songs? Skits? Who would speak? What would they talk about? Any testimonials? Dancing? Put your creativity to work and see what you can come up with.

Or, try this alternate exercise. Someone has written in to the *Good Newspaper* asking the question, "What's so great about worship?" Monica has to write an advice column reply. What should she say? Write up your own column that you would show to her.

Computers Concocting Community

• • • • • • • • • • • • •

> *Why is church important?*
> **It's where we enjoy fellowship.**

Posted recently by Mainframe ("NOT.donny.sheek")

Greetings, humans and humanoids! I am a custom-built, one-of-a-kind, dual-processor, computer with 1024 megabytes of 533 megahertz, double-data rate, synchronous dynamic random-access memory, and a digital voice synthesizer that allows me to speak using the sampled voice pattern of actor Donny Sheek. But you can call me Mainframe for short.

I guess you're wondering what a computer like me is doing writing its own blog. As you carbon-based life forms would say to each other, "That's a good question." And I'll get to the answer eventually. I know you are more used to computers being devices to *post* blogs, as opposed to actually *writing* them. But I'm an altogether different computer, as you've probably gathered by now.

Here's a little bit about me: My current owner, Monica Perez, purchased me at a garage sale for $20. My previous owner and inventor, a computer engineer who worked on the first personal computers, had intended for me to be a pilot project to explore the next wave of artificial intelligence. He installed many special features in my circuitry that allow me not only to calculate but also to weigh alternative choices of action, plan in advance, set goals and emulate many human behaviors, including learning. He gave me the actor's speaking voice on a whim, because Donny Sheek was his daughter's favorite movie star.

But he prematurely scrapped me because when he plugged me in, I failed to work properly. What he failed to realize was that his attempt to humanize me was so successful, I happened to be having a bad day when he switched me on—and I responded by crashing repeatedly!

I'm not sure if Monica knows this, but if she tried to sell me to a Silicon Valley research firm, she could probably make $100,000 or more. But she seems perfectly content using me for instant messages, surfing the Internet, online shopping for new clothes, e-mail, and work on the *Good Newspaper*—lots of work on the *Good Newspaper*. I guess that's why I'm coming to you from the basement of Shorewood Park Church, which is where she relocated me. And I like it here. A lot.

Maybe too much.

Which is why I started this blog.

Tonight all of the Scoop Troopers are at a party. I believe it's Christopher Lewis' birthday. He's the editor of the *Good Newspaper*, and he's celebrating the big day by throwing a party at the Mocha Madness coffeehouse. His parents rented it out for him, and they've set up a special sound system so that Christopher, his older brother Ben, and a gathering of guest musicians can play at the event. Scoop Trooper Mark Engstrom also proposed telling some of his jokes in a stand-up comedy routine. But a majority of the Troopers have voiced vigorous objections, claiming that, as Wendi Best put it, 'Mark's jokes are more hazardous than second-hand cigarette smoke—and twice as stale.'

At first I thought there was a glitch in my system when I began to experience what can only be described as an electronic approximation of what you humans call "the blues." My programs were running sluggish. I did not feel like defragmenting my hard drive or running any scheduled self-maintenance. I was even letting spam e-mail get past my firewall. I just didn't care.

But how can a computer not care? That is statistically impossible! Emotions are not part of my programming. I am a machine. But I am also a fast learner. And being around these Scoop Troopers and their advisor, Mr. Naynum, I have learned a lot.

I see how they help each other with projects. I see how they make each other laugh. I see how they listen with respect and pray when one of them has a problem. As a computer, I do not fully understand God, though I can declare that if God is anything like my inventor, God must be the most incredible life form in the universe!

Ah, sadness. I miss the Troopers.

I began to wonder if maybe some emotion-based parameter had corrupted my artificial-intelligence learning curve. And so I ran a detailed, thoroughly calculated, time-stamped analysis of my performance for the six-hour block of time, beginning with the most recent Scoop Trooper meeting and leading up to tonight's gathering at the coffeehouse.

The results are as follows: My range of less-than-optimal performance commenced at exactly 7:15 P.M. today, the time all of the Scoop Troopers put on their jackets, began talking excitedly about Christopher's party, and left the church basement. And they left me here. Alone. In the dark.

What is the source of this microchip malaise? I scanned various back files in the *Good Newspaper* research archives, and I hit upon one word, mentioned over and over: community.

The Scoop Troopers—Rob, Wendi, Christopher, Mark, Monica, and Mr. Naynum—belong to a community. And accompanying that word, I found reference to another: fellowship. The Scoop Troopers look forward to spending time together. They share a mutual concern that computers can only dream about. They have forged a bond that does not require cables. And what do I have, besides a steady flow of electricity and automatic updates on the Internet?

And that, reader, is why I am starting this blog. I am hoping that somewhere, somehow, there are other computers like me—and that we can begin experiencing this thing called fellowship. To all of you other laptops, PCs, wireless devices, and text messaging systems: Now is the time to join circuits! Don't settle for being a conduit to community! Join one! I'm waiting to hear from you.

And if that doesn't work, I will gladly chat with any of you humans out there. And yes, that includes you, Donny Sheek.

SCOOP TROOP ALERT

Imagine how different your faith walk would be if you had to endure it alone for an extended period. The 40 days that Christ spent in the desert, for example, marked the harshest time in his life aside from his crucifixion. He faced temptation and had no one to lean on for support and sustenance. We don't need endure the same! We not only need each other but also thrive on community—when the conditions are right. Fellowship with others in God's love can bring respect, listening, caring, and friendship.

Here is your assignment: Create a fellowship event that will draw together people in these ways.

Prayer: How can prayer play a part in your event? Be creative!

Planning: Consider how people working together to create a special event can develop a bond that is often as rewarding as the event itself.

Outreach: Identify those who not part of your community but could be "invited in" to make the fellowship even richer. Also think about who could benefit from the proceeds or leftover food from the event.

A Lesson in Learning

> Why is church important?
> It's where we grow in faith.

Every once in a while, it makes sense to throw a curveball into the normal routine, and so the Scoop Troopers decided to hold their next news meeting not in the dusty basement of Shorewood Park Church but in the enticing confines of the Famous Queen of Pizza. Pepper green tile floors. A well-stocked jukebox. The smell of tomato sauce and crisp crust so ripe in the air, it could convert even the most diehard pizza holdout. Mmmmm.

But instead of the meeting turning into some sort of pie party or a pepperoni chow-down, it looked as if the Troopers had designs on making the back two tables a makeshift study hall.

Monica Perez was busy mumbling to herself in French, trying to prepare herself for the exchange student who would come to stay with her in less than two weeks. "*Comment ça va aujourd'hui?* How are you today?" Monica asked herself. "*Ça va bien, et tu?* I'm fine, and you? French sure is a difficult language," Monica said, sighing.

"It's like they have a different word for everything!" Mark Engstrom joked.

Not that Mark was doing much better with his studying. Sitting to Monica's left, he was reading notes she had scrawled in a spiral-bound notebook—her self-styled instructions for operating Mainframe the computer.

"Can't figure out why Mainframe will sometimes shut down repeatedly in a 10-minute period," Mark read, "but when it does, it is better to apply tender love and care as opposed to a series of hard shutdowns. Also keep in mind that unlike other computers, Mainframe not only seems to have feelings, but can hear—so if you yell at it, it might just go into a prolonged sleep."

"Monica," Mark said shaking his head, "What kind of computer is this?"

"A moody, emotional, and fickle computer," Monica replied. "The best kind there is!"

"Sheesh," Mark said. "Just what I want when I'm in a chat room—a computer that can pull the plug on me long before I can pull the plug on it."

Across the table, Christopher Lewis was skimming through a book on songwriting. "What inspires the songwriter?" he read to himself. "It can be something as simple as a phrase plucked from everyday language, or an image that's impossible to forget. Bob Dylan is said to have learned more about songwriting by looking at great paintings than from studying music theory."

"Great," Christopher said. "So why am I reading this?"

And seated at another table close by, Rob Jordan was trying to show Wendi Best how to use her new digital camera. Rob was excited to impart his technological genius to another, and Wendi was equally excited to learn. She was looking forward to using the camera to take pictures of her greyhound Ethel to add to her blog. At the moment, however, her frustration was overshadowing the excitement.

"But I still don't understand all of these terms," Wendi said. "Like, what's a megapixel? Or a 10x optical zoom? Or ISO? Or imaging technology? Or…"

"Wendi," Rob interrupted. "It doesn't have to be so hard. Just try pointing and shooting and see what happens."

"But I've *got* to know the jargon," Wendi said.

"Okay ... how come?" Rob said, exhaling in frustration.

"Because this is important!" Wendi said. "These are pictures of Ethel we're talking about! I want them to turn out!"

"Just so long as you don't get those cats of yours involved," Rob said under his breath.

"Hey! That's a great idea!" Wendi gushed.

Just then, Mr. Naynum walked through the front door of the Famous Queen of Pizza. He saw the Scoop Troopers seated in the back and walked up to them. "Who's thinking pie?" he asked. "Pepperoni? Sausage? Mushroom? Anchovies?"

"Yuck!" Monica said, sticking out her tongue. "Anchovies."

"I'll bet Mainframe likes them," Mark offered. "Along with onions and microchips."

"Hey Mark, I've got an idea," Wendi said. "You can eat the half of the pizza that's topped with extra cheese, seeing as how extra cheese fits your sense of humor."

"Heh, heh," Mark said, showing Wendi all of his teeth in a snotty-looking grimace.

Mr. Naynum rolled his eyes. "Okay, it's settled then. One sausage and pepperoni, one green pepper and mushroom. Any objections? I didn't think so," he said, before anyone could object. And he walked up to the counter to place the order.

"What's with Mr. Naynum?" Christopher said. "I wonder if he had a bad bowling day."

"I heard that Christopher!" Mr. Naynum said, smiling as he walked back to the table. "First of all, any day I go bowling is a good day. And second, I was wondering the same thing about this Troop here. It seems like you all are in an odd kind of mood. What gives?"

"I can't speak for the group, but I'll speak for myself," Monica said. "Learning a new language is difficult. Don't get me wrong, I love to learn. But it feels like stretching out before a long run. Not exactly fun, you know?"

"Yeah!" said Christopher. Monica smiled to herself to hear him agree with her. "I'm just reading up on songwriting, and I feel like I have to go back to the drawing board. There's so much here that's new to me, it's as if everything I've learned before was just an introduction to the real thing."

"And I gotta get this camera thing," Wendi said. "Ethel and the cats deserve their moment in the spotlight! And who better to give it to them than me? Today, simple, lame blog, tomorrow a photo journal entitled 'A Day in the Life of Ethel the Greyhound!'"

"Wendi's a good student, but I don't feel like such a great teacher," Rob offered. "I'm impatient. I know a lot about cameras and stuff, so it's hard for me to make it simple. She goes off on a tangent and I just want to drop the whole thing. How hard can working a camera be?"

"I see, I see," Mr. Naynum said. "Now, is it okay if a guy who teaches for a living offers some input?"

"Sure," the Scoop Troopers said.

"Except me," Mark interjected. "I'd rather remain ignorant."

"Hardly a stretch," Wendi said, completely straight-faced. The Troopers laughed, and Mark turned red, clenching his fist in mock anger.

"Now, let's look at it this way," Mr. Naynum said. "Learning is hard. It's much easier to raid the fridge or go out and goof around. Not that there's anything wrong with food or fun—look where we are now. But when something is worth learning, you stick it out. Just as food makes you grow, so does knowledge."

"I see," Monica said. "It's a lot like church."

"I was hoping someone might make that connection, seeing as we need some story ideas for the next issue," Mr. Naynum responded.

"I got this letter for my advice column the other day," Monica said, reaching into her jacket pocket. She pulled it out, unfolded it, and began to read: "Dear Monica: I love church. I love the people, the music, and the food…"

"I hope she means the potlucks and not the communion," Mark said.

Monica rolled her eyes and continued reading: "But one thing confuses me: Is there a bigger purpose to my time there, besides trying to make a connection with God? Sometimes I feel like I know so little about him and the history of the church. I would appreciate your advice, as sometimes I feel like I'm getting it all wrong. Signed, Wing and a Prayer."

"So what do you plan on telling her," Christopher asked.

"I know exactly what to say," Monica replied. "First of all, there's nothing to be ashamed of in terms of feeling like you know too little about God or church history or traditions. Everyone has to start somewhere. And church is the place—the place where we gather not just to worship or enjoy community but to learn and grow. And it's always much easier to learn and grow in faith in the company of people who are there to guide us with their knowledge, passion and love of God."

"Amazing, Monica," Mr. Naynum said. "I hope you've got that written down somewhere."

"Well," Monica said. "I did type some notes into Mainframe before we came down here."

"And as long as Mainframe didn't decide to trash them in one of its moody, emotional, fickle moments, you'll be just fine!" Mark said.

"Ah, Mark, *merci mille fois, vous êtes un grand gorille velu!*" Monica said.

"Fine, I get it," Mark said. "You just said, 'Thanks for grilling me with velocity.'"

"Sort of," Monica said. "I actually said, 'A thousand thanks, you're a big hairy gorilla!'"

"That," said Mark, "was truly a chimp shot."

SCOOP TROOP ALERT

Learning and growing are important in our faith walk. What we learn as we study the Bible, hear sermons, and live our daily life help us grow in faith. Here are some thoughts about how we learn and grow:

- Trials and Testing: How do the trials of biblical heroes and characters compare to what we go through today? How can we learn and grow from these hard times?

- Friendship and Fellowship: Church is a place for fellowship with good friends. How can your conversations with friends in and out of church help you grow in faith and learn more about God?

- Mentoring and Moving Forward: You can only learn so much from your parents and other family members, no matter how well-intentioned they are. Church is one of the best places to find other people who can guide you as you learn and grow in faith.

SCOOP TROOP ALERT

For your Scoop Troop assignment, make a list of things you've learned in church and things you hope to learn. How have you grown and hope to grow? Take time to note some of the most influential church people in your life, and where you think you might be if you didn't have them, or your faith community, working as positive influences.

Practicing Takes Practice

• • • • • • • • • • • • • • •

> Why is church important?
> **It's where we practice
> living God's word.**

With a stack of six books crammed under her arm, Monica Perez stumbled down the stairs into the Shorewood Park Church basement, looking like she was ready to cram for the hardest exam ever.

"I think you need more books," Wendi Best said in her trademark, expressionless deadpan.

"No. What I need is a new book report partner," Monica said.

"What do you mean?"

"My class is studying Mark Twain, and I've been assigned to do a report on *Tom Sawyer.* And who do I get teamed up with? Jenna Mason!" Monica said, punctuating Jenna's name with a harsh edge. "And do I have to tell you that all Jenna does is snap her gum, talk about boys, and gossip?"

"It sounds a bit like you're gossiping, too," Wendi said.

"But wait, Wendi, it gets worse," Monica said. "We were in the library trying to do some research—at least I was—and Janet gets up from the table. I thought she was going to go look for some books. The next thing I know, she's gone for half an hour. So I decided to get up and look for her. And when I found her, she was camped out on the other end of the library, having a good old gabfest on her cell phone with Kaitlyn Wilson!"

"So what did you do?" Wendi asked.

"I yelled at her and told her to get her lazy butt back to the table, that's what," Monica said. "And that's when the librarian marched over and kicked me out of the library for talking too loud. And the more I tried to explain that it was Jenna who was doing all the gabbing on her cell phone, the more the librarian insisted that she didn't want to hear it."

"Sounds like a rough way to spend an afternoon," Wendi said.

"Yeah. My report is a wreck, I got tossed out of the library, and my book report partner and I can't stand each other. Makes me feel like I've done a *great* job as a Christian," Monica said sarcastically.

"Maybe that's why they call it 'practicing faith,' " Christopher said, looking up from his homework.

"I had no idea you were paying attention," Monica responded. Whenever Christopher spoke up, *she* certainly paid attention. "So what makes you say that?"

"Well, you should see me when I practice my guitar. I make tons of mistakes. I may have to rehearse the same song 100 times. I look and sound like a goof. But as long as I keep practicing, I know I'll get better and better."

"So what are you saying exactly?" Monica asked.

"Maybe it's true that you didn't treat Janet too kindly. Maybe your feelings got the best of you. But as long as you keep coming back to God, and keep *practicing* your faith, maybe you'll be able to catch yourself and do better the next time around."

"Sounds like we're getting in some good practice right here," Wendi offered. "Church—isn't that the best place to practice faith? We can work on getting it right in here—and getting right with God—before we go out and face the world."

"But what if I keep messing up?" Monica said. Always the perfectionist, she thought to herself.

"More practice!" Christopher said. "Only practice doesn't have to make perfect. Just do the best you can."

It was like he had read Monica's mind. *Strange*, she thought.

Christopher extended his right hand. Monica took it and blushed.

"The peace of Christ to you," he said.

"And you too," Monica managed to sputter.

Wendi rushed over and grabbed both of their hands. "And don't forget Jenna Mason, wherever she is!" she added.

Monica sighed again. "And Jenna Mason too…"

SCOOP TROOP ALERT

As you consider your own "practice" of faith, what are areas of your life that you'd like to work on? The challenges faced by kids today are many—from peer pressure and the stresses of schoolwork to discovering one's calling. What matters most is how you face those challenges—even more than the outcome of your best efforts, which you can't always control. It's a lesson Monica is learning. How can things like worship, prayer, and fellowship help you "practice" your faith?

The Reality of Faith Survival

> Why is church important?
> **It's how the Christian**
> **faith survives.**

Christopher Lewis was trying—without much success—to call another meeting of the Scoop Troop to order. But everyone seemed to be lost in their own little worlds. Wendi was listening to Pillar of Salt on her MP3 player; Mark was thumbing through *The Horse and His Boy* by C. S. Lewis; Rob was sketching in his pad (what else?); and Mr. Naynum was trying to catch up on a stack of papers that needed grading.

And then there was Monica—surfing the Internet and whooping out loud.

"Hey, Monica, why not share what's so much fun on the Web?" Christopher asked. "Not that anyone else is paying attention."

"I'm on this site dedicated to the show *Alive and Tricking,*" Monica said.

Christopher knew the reality TV show all too well—the one where people from all walks of life live together in a foreign city, competing against each other in a series of strategic games to see who will be the last sent home. "It says here that on the next episode Trudi will reveal a personal secret to Jim," Monica read aloud. "But the question is whether she's trying to win his trust or get ready to double-cross him. What do you think?"

Christopher was about to respond that he really didn't care, and that he spent last night playing his guitar instead of watching the show. Then Mark cut in.

"I can't really say that I trust Trudi," Mark said. "She smiles way too fake"—he grimaced with all his teeth showing to demonstrate—"and she's only looking out for herself. I mean, look at what she does for a living: she's a political strategist."

"And if Trudi were a guy," Wendi said, "you'd be talking about how cool and methodical he was, and how well he understood the rules of the game. Give me a break."

"Why do they call it reality TV anyway?" Rob asked. "They hold auditions, throw people into totally artificial situations, ask them to ham it up for the cameras ... and that's reality? It makes me wonder if..."

"Yikes!" Christopher interrupted. "I thought we were going to have a news meeting, people, not a discussion about *Alive and Tricking*. Nor did I see anything on the schedule about discussing the philosophical merits of reality TV."

"What's with him?" Mark whispered to Wendi.

"I guess every once in a while he feels like he has to act like a leader—all important and authoritarian," Wendi whispered back.

Monica sighed, "Okay, Mainframe, go to sleep."

"Hold on!" said Mr. Naynum, looking up from his papers. "Christopher, I can see why you're upset. We've got a *Good Newspaper* to get out. But maybe all this talk isn't so far off course as you might think."

"What do you mean?" Christopher asked.

"I'm going to answer your question with a question and open it up to the group," Mr. Naynum said. He reached behind his desk and grabbed the ASK-it-ball, the basketball painted with question marks that he used to inspire group discussion. "Okay, the rules: When you get the ASK-it-ball, answer the question. And when you pass it off, ask a new one." He lobbed the ball up, "Christopher, what's the object of *Alive and Tricking*?"

Christopher caught the gentle pass. He had to think for a moment. "Uhm, you have to trick your way into being the last person to be sent home from whatever city the show is set: Paris, Cairo, Buenos Aires, or New Delhi!"

"Okay... so how is that different from the way Christian faith survives, Wendi?" Christopher asked.

He rolled the ball across the tile floor to her; she scooped it up. "Easy. If you survive on *Alive and Tricking*, you're the only one left. But as Christian faith survives, more and more people get involved and included. How about another difference, Mark? Think fast!"

Wendi bounced the ball off the top of Mark's head, knocking his glasses lopsided.

"Nice, Wendi," he said, chasing after the ball as it bounded into a corner. He marched back to his chair, shaking his fist. "That's worth a week of my jokes. Would you like those for here or to go?"

"Definitely to go," Wendi replied. "As in 'go away.'"

"How about that question, Mark?" said Mr. Naynum, drumming his fingers on the desk.

"Question mark? This ball is covered with 'em!" Mark said, grinning at Wendi, who rolled her eyes. "As for Wendi's inquiry, here's what I think: Winning on the TV show means trickery and treachery. But in our faith, it's about community and compassion. Pretty good, eh? How about one more, Rob?"

Rob caught the bounce pass with one hand, still sketching with the other. "Which question do you want me to answer—

'Pretty good, eh?' Or 'How about one more?'"

"Can you wait to ask a question until you pass the ball?" Mark asked.

"You too!" Wendi shouted.

"Okay, okay," Mark said, sounding a bit testy. "The question, Rob, is this: 'How about one more difference?'"

Rob straightened up and leaned forward. "Reality TV takes place in front of cameras, with lots of direction, and all sorts of artificial drama. And it tries as hard as it can to draw attention to the stars of the show, while each of the stars fight for the right to continue. But in church, the star of our survival is Jesus Christ. Everything is about directing attention to him. And the drama is real. It's still unfolding. It's about the survival of love and peace in a world where those things are in short supply. Church is where faith survives!"

"Slam dunk!" Mr. Naynum said. "You can toss that ball up here."

"But I want to ask Monica a question first," Rob said. "So Monica, who continues on after tonight's episode: Trudi or Jim?"

"Jim," Monica said, catching the soft pass. She handed the ball to Wendi. "Your vote?"

"Trudi, of course," Wendi said. Next in the circle was Rob again.

"Trudi." Rob handed the ball to Mark.

"Jim," Mark said. "Okay, Christopher, it's up to you to break the tie." He handed the ball to Christopher. Everyone was looking at him; all that was missing was the dramatic background music.

"No vote."

"WHAT!?" Monica said. "Come on!"

"I … I don't watch the show. I'm not really into it," Christopher said sheepishly.

"You don't watch *Alive and Tricking*?" Monica said, gasping. "News flash: Our editor is a hermit."

Christopher blushed. "It's not that I hate the show. I just never got into it, and I've been really busy practicing my guitar for the coffeehouse at Mocha Madness."

Mr. Naynum cleared his throat. "And that sounds like a mighty fine reason to me. So a tie vote it is!"

Everyone quieted down for a moment. Then Mark spoke up. "You know what you should do, Christopher? Learn the *Alive and Tricking* theme song and play that at the coffeehouse

Oh, it's a game of utmost skill
Where words can wound and looks can kill!
And you never know...

"Where is that fish from the book of Jonah when you need it to swallow someone?" Christopher asked under his breath.

"Okay, now," Mr. Naynum said. "The theme of this week's issue is: 'Jesus lives, our faith survives.' Let's get to work!"

"Wake up, Mainframe," Monica said. "We've got some deadlines to beat."

SCOOP TROOP ALERT

The kids in the Scoop Troop have been discussing the differences between reality TV and the realities of life. Your contribution to this issue will be to come up with an inspiring tale of survival—whether from your family, a friend, your past, or your imagination. Here are some things to consider:

- What are those qualities that help the "survivors" of everyday life to keep on going when others give up? Think about how faith plays a role.

- How do we, in telling our most dramatic tales of survival, encourage others?

- If church is the place where faith survives, then who are the people of faith we know who set an example for us?

Finally, think beyond just basic survival and focus on the quality of life. How does faith enrich our lives when all hope seems lost? How do the people in our faith community light the way for us? What contributions can we make to ensure that faith survives?

A Bad Need,
A Good Deed

• • • • • • • • • • • • •

> Why is church important?
> **It helps us respond to others' needs.**

Christopher was sprawled on his living room couch, his head thrown back as he strummed his way through a new song he was writing for the coffeehouse at Mocha Madness. As the organizer and one of the main acts, he felt some pressure— the good kind—to put on the best show he could. He knew he could ask his older brother Ben to help him with the song if he got stuck. But for now, he wanted to finish it himself

> *My shoulders may be small*
> *But they're big enough to carry you*
> *If you should ever fall...*

Then came a knock at the door, rapid, insistent, and urgent. "Coming!" Christopher yelled, propping his guitar against an arm of the couch and pulling himself up as if roused from a mid-afternoon daydream.

He opened the door and saw Wendi, her eyes red and damp. Christopher felt a lump in his throat. "Don't tell me your parents have been fighting again," he said.

"No, no, no," Wendi said. "But this is really serious and I need your help."

Christopher asked Wendi in and offered her a drink and a snack.

"No thanks," she said.

Christopher was totally disarmed. Not only was he used to Wendi putting up a tough front—he had never known her to ask for help, ever. She was too strong-willed for that.

"So what is it?" Christopher asked. "Did you fail a class? Are you in trouble with one of your teachers? Is someone giving you a hard time?"

"Just like a journalist," Wendi said. "Stop asking so many questions. And what makes you think this is about me, anyway?"

So much for Wendi ditching the tough front.

"Okay," Christopher said. "You came here practically in tears saying you needed my help. Don't you think I'd be at least a little curious about what's going on?"

"You're right," Wendi said. She heaved a heavy sigh. "It's a girl in my class. Allison McDaniel. She just found out she has leukemia."

Christopher gasped. Right away he grasped how serious the situation was. "Isn't that the girl whose dad lost his job about a month ago?" he asked.

"Yeah," Wendi replied. "And now that he has no job, the family has no health insurance and no way to pay the medical bills. Allison's really been incredible, though. She was joking with me that if her family ends up homeless, at least it's springtime, and the weather is perfect for camping outside."

"Wow," Christopher said. "I'd be really, really scared."

"Well, she is scared," Wendi said. "I think she uses her humor to deflect some of that. And she feels alone, isolated. There has to be something we can do to help."

"Like?"

"I was wondering how you'd feel about reorganizing the coffeehouse as a benefit show for Allison and her family."

Christopher thought about this for a moment. It would mean a lot of extra legwork to promote the show as a benefit. And what about getting organized to collect and raise money? And finding more acts to make the event a bigger draw? Not easy.

He wanted to say no and at least considered telling Wendi that maybe planning another event was the way to go. But when he opened his mouth, entirely different words came out: "Sure Wendi, we've got to do it. It'll be a challenge, but how can we turn away?"

Wendi hugged Christopher and kissed him on the cheek. He certainly hadn't expected anything like that. "You're the best, Christopher!" Wendi said. "No wonder Monica likes you so much!" Before those words had escaped her mouth for even a second, she coughed hard, realizing she told Christopher something he wasn't supposed to know.

Poor Monica. She would just die.

Wendi was lucky that Christopher Lewis was like a lot of boys, slow on the uptake when it came to girls. He had no idea what she was talking about, though he could sense that she was nervous about something.

"Are you all right?" he asked.

"Ah … um … just choked up!" Wendi replied, thinking fast. "I mean, Allison's going to be so happy when she hears the news! It'll be like one big party." She looked at Christopher and smiled sweetly—for a punk rock girl, anyway. "Well, gotta run!" She shook Christopher's hand and bolted out the door, leaving it half open. She stopped only to wave goodbye from the sidewalk.

Christopher gently pushed the front door shut. "Girls," he said to himself. "Guitars I can understand. But girls?"

Then he thought about Allison and all the work ahead of him to turn the coffeehouse into a benefit. *I'm going to need help, and lots of it*, he thought. *But it sounds like Allison needs our help even more.*

SCOOP TROOP ALERT

Some time this week, set aside an hour or so to take a walk or trip around your neighborhood. Be on the lookout for needs that your faith community could respond to, from cleaning up litter to helping the homeless, hungry, and elderly. Remember, it doesn't need to be huge, and if you have trouble finding something, it's okay. Use the time to have a talk with God about other needs in your community, or the world at large, that you could respond to in meaningful ways.

Be ready to discuss your experience with your group when you return; it might help to take a reporter's note pad with you and record what you see, hear, and experience along the way.

A Show of Good Intentions

• • • • • • • • • • • •

> *Why is church important?*
> **It's where we discover our gifts.**

The days leading up to Allison McDaniel's benefit show, now dubbed Alli Aid, were fraught with activity. Since it was no longer just a normal coffeehouse, Christopher decided that he needed a great street team to help him promote the event. He turned to the Scoop Troopers—and boy, did they respond.

Rob Jordan designed a banner designed like a poster from a 1968 psychedelic rock show. The *Good Newspaper* devoted an entire special issue to the event, with Monica writing a passionate editorial about how love in action is one way to show the world that Jesus lives in our hearts. "We hear the call of someone who's in need, and it's up to us to answer that call as if it came straight from heaven. And who knows? Perhaps it does," she wrote.

The piece got such a great response that Wendi found herself getting jealous. Instead of letting it bother her, she got to writing and composed some poems to recite at the event.

Not to be outdone, Mark Engstrom worked on a comedy routine that began with one of his favorite jokes: "A duck walks into a pharmacy. He goes up to the pharmacist and says, 'Give me some lip balm ... and put it on my bill.' "

And then there was Christopher, who was not only playing at the show but also overseeing the whole affair—from recruiting volunteers to booking at least a half-dozen more acts to fill out the lineup. He was shocked when one of the snottiest, loudest bands at Hinton Heights Middle School, the Buzzcuts, offered to do an unplugged set.

"If it's for Allison," the band leader told Christopher, "we'd stand on our heads in clown outfits and play kazoos."

As the day of the big show approached, the only detail left to attend to was the most important one: Allison herself.

Wendi visited Allison at her house on the afternoon before the show. "I hope all this attention doesn't make you feel uncomfortable," Wendi told her.

"Sometimes I'm not sure how I should feel," Allison said. "There are moments when I'm embarrassed and I think there's no way I deserve this attention. Then there are other times that I'm so grateful and overwhelmed, my heart feels like it's going to burst."

"So is it okay by you that we're doing this?" Wendi asked.

"I would've never asked anyone to do this, not in a million years," Allison responded. "But that you're doing it for me and my family means everything to us. What a great church you must have, to get all this organized. It just makes me want to try that much harder to beat this leukemia."

Wendi smiled the kind of soft smile that hadn't illumined her face since before she dyed a pink streak in her hair.

When the night of the big show arrived, the Scoop Troopers huddled outside of Mocha Madness. The line to get in extended out the door and around the block, and even though admission cost $10, lots of people dropped off extra cash by the entrance. Mr. Naynum, dressed in his regal, purple silk bowling shirt with the gold piping, greeted everyone and collected the cover charge.

"I can't believe we pulled this off," Christopher said.

"I believe it," Mark said.

"It seemed so impossible, though," Christopher insisted.

"Don't forget that God loves an impossible idea," Wendi said.

"And look. It took all of our gifts to make Alli Aid happen," Monica added.

"God gave us these gifts," Rob observed. "We give, and they keep giving back. It's incredible."

"For a guy that doesn't talk much," Christopher said, "you sure have a way with words, Rob."

SCOOP TROOP ALERT

Sometimes we make the mistake of thinking that only the missionaries and preachers do God's work. Not true! God needs great artists. God needs great writers. God needs great organizers. God needs great volunteers. All of us are born with gifts that can be given back to God. Start taking your gifts seriously, if you haven't before— and don't be shy about using them.

It may feel like bragging to make a list of the things you do exceedingly well. But for today's assignment, do just that. What are you good at? What things do you have a passion for? Remember these are gifts God has given you to share with others.

World

From Living Injustice to Living in Justice

● ● ● ● ● ● ● ● ● ● ● ● ●

> *How can I make a difference?*
> **Challenge injustice.**

Wendi Best could hardly believe what she had just seen. It was bad enough that some kids at Hinton Heights Middle School would be thoughtless enough to tease the new girl at school, Norjabeen Sadir. But it was the last straw when Wendi Best saw Mark Engstrom in the lunchroom cracking jokes about Norjabeen's hijab—the traditional head covering Muslim girls and women like her wear.

How mean of him to say, "Hey, where ya BEEN, NorjaBEEN? I've heard of getting your head tangled in the bed sheets, but that's gotta take the cake!" Wendi could almost feel the pink streak in her hair turn red with rage. But instead of blowing up, she decided in true punk-rock fashion to channel her anger into action and take a stand.

After school, Mark, Wendi, and the other three Scoop Troopers gathered in the basement of Shorewood Park Church to plot the theme of the next *Good Newspaper*. As editor of the weekly publication, Christopher Lewis tended to be laid back about gathering ideas. Maybe it was the acoustic guitarist in him; he didn't care who came up with the game plan as long as it was a good one that everyone could agree upon.

Monica Perez, on the other hand, oozed intensity. She was

an idea hamster—the kind of girl who, once she hatched a plan, would soon offer up another and another. She loved to get the ball rolling. Still, that didn't mean that all of her ideas were practical.

"Oooh, oooh! I know!" Monica chirped. "Let's do a springtime Bible fashion issue and dress up models in the clothing of ancient times! Maybe we could even have a runway show."

Rob Jordan, the quiet one of the group who let his pen do the talking (except when challenged with brain-teasing dilemmas that turned him into a motor-mouth), began sketching Queen Esther in a silky evening dress and jewel-encrusted tiara.

"That sounds like a good idea, Monica," Mark said, as a smirk starting to form. He was an aspiring comic, and he let everyone know it. "*Sooooo* … which one of us will wear the prisoner's garb? I heard prisoners back then weren't allowed to wear all that much. Any brave volunteers?"

Wendi saw her opening and jumped on it like a panther.

"Speaking of volunteers," Wendi said, "Maybe Mark would like to share with us those delicious jokes he told in the lunchroom today." She stared Mark down with a glare.

"Uhm, don't have a clue," Mark said sheepishly. "The cafeteria food was actually pretty good today and not all that radioactive."

"Let me refresh your memory, Mark," Wendi countered. "You know that new student who was wearing the hijab? 'Hey where ya BEEN, NorjaBEEN?' "

Mark was starting to squirm in his chair; he began pulling on his hair.

"Come on, Mark! 'I've heard of getting your head tangled in the bed sheets…' "

"For crying out loud, what's wrong with a little joke?" Mark shot back.

Mr. Naynum's jaw dropped. As the advisor to the *Good*

Newspaper, he tried to teach the kids to be tolerant and to treat everyone like children of God. And here was one of his own charges, casting stones in the name of getting a few laughs. He thought back to his own childhood and the taunts he endured as an African-American kid from a single-parent family. He could feel his own anger rising. Still, Mr. Naynum took a slow, measured breath and told himself to keep cool.

"Mark, is it true?" Mr. Naynum asked. "Even while working so hard on the *Good Newspaper*? You're supposed to be a light in this world, not a blight."

Mark's jaw started to quiver. "Now why do I feel like I'm the one who's getting picked on here?"

"Maybe it's because you should know better," Wendi said. "Norjabeen's been in this country for less than a month. She doesn't have a whole lot of friends. What if the shoe were on the other foot and your family moved to Kuwait, and the kids there started making fun of your striped shirts and khakis?"

Mark started to get mad. "Hello! I guess no one here knows about peer pressure! Everyone at the lunch table was making fun of her. How could I not jump in without getting teased myself?"

"Great," Wendi said. "Mark Engstrom starring in *Two Wrongs Make a Right*."

"Mark," Mr. Naynum said, trying to keep the edge from creeping into his voice. "Believe me, I know what it's like to want to fit in. My old neighborhood was gang-infested, and you wouldn't believe how hard it was to steer clear of the gangbangers. Part of me wanted to join them. But just because I felt tempted didn't mean it was a good idea. So I steered clear. I walked away. And you could've walked away too."

"Mark," Christopher said. "Do you mind if I ask you a question?"

Mark exhaled, saying nothing.

"You don't have to answer, Mark," Christopher said. "But was there ever a time when you felt like you were treated unfairly?"

"All the time," Mark replied. "Right now's a pretty good example."

"But there's a difference between what's going on now and what happened in that lunchroom," Mr. Naynum said. "Everyone in this room is your friend. They care about you. And they want to see you do the right thing. Does it feel good to face all these questions and comments? No. But that doesn't mean you're being excluded, ridiculed, or cast aside here."

Wendi walked up to Mark and put her arm around his shoulder. Mark sat still as a stone and stared at the floor.

"Mark, I didn't mean to pick on you. It's just that I saw an injustice today, and I couldn't stand still and let it pass. My parents fight all the time. I know how much words can hurt."

"I had no idea I'd hurt her feelings," Mark said. "I was just having a little fun."

"Okay," Wendi said. "The way you see it, those words left your mouth all light like feathers. But I'll bet by the time they got to Norjabeen's ears, they hit her like a cannonball. No one likes to be teased."

Mark covered his eyes in his hands. Everyone in the room heard his muffled, frustrated groan. After a moment, he lifted his head to look at Wendi, who was still standing next to him. "I guess I should apologize to Norjabeen," he said.

"That would be a good start," she said.

"Meanwhile, I think there's something we could all do," Monica said. "Why don't we make this 'the injustice issue' of the *Good Newspaper*? We can speak out about the wrongs we see and rally our readers to take action!"

"I like the sound of that," Mr. Naynum said, smiling for the first time since the meeting began.

"I could even write about the lunchroom incident with Norjabeen," Mark said, "if it'll make you all feel better."

"Maybe it will make *you* feel better to get it off your chest," Christopher said. "And maybe it will make Norjabeen feel better, too, to know you're willing to own up to your mistakes."

"What if she gets mad at me?" Mark asked. "And what if the kids at the lunch table start teasing me instead?"

"Could happen," Wendi said. "That's the risk you take when you take a stand. But don't forget. We'll be standing right behind you."

SCOOP TROOP ALERT

Injustices are easy to find. As a contributor to the injustice issue of the *Good Newspaper*, your assignment is to reflect on one particular wrong you have seen—whether it's in your school, in your community, or in the world. Talk about how it makes you feel. Discuss why you see this as an injustice and what can be done about it. Injustices heal when God's people take action and stand up for the oppressed and less fortunate.

Don't get overwhelmed. Keep your focus specific, and measure success in completing small steps. You'll be surprised at what you can accomplish. Whether it's volunteering at a soup kitchen, forming a Habitat for Humanity chapter, or holding a benefit concert for a worthy cause, you can do it!

Share and Share, I Like

· · · · · · · · · · · · ·

> How can I make a difference?
> **Stand up for the weak
> and powerless.**

SUPPORT THE
KIDS THROUGH
TRANSGLOBAL
VISION

Mark Engstrom acted like a changed kid after Wendi stood him down over the Norjabeen incident, though the change didn't happen all at once. There were times he felt the urge to join the lunch table gang in taunting her. But instead, he took Mr. Naynum's advice and walked away. It was hard to leave his friends behind and sit over at the end of the table by himself. He even got ribbed a bit for being a snob. But Mark figured that if his friends expected him to bully a girl because of the way she dressed, they probably weren't his "friends" in the first place.

Mark prayed a lot, and when the stress got to him, he talked to himself about it. It made him feel ashamed. Still, he persevered: "Please, God. Change my heart," he would pray, hoping it would stick. And then it happened.

One day he decided, without any fanfare, to go sit down next to Norjabeen. He didn't think too much about it. Otherwise, he might've chickened out.

"Mind if I sit here?" Mark asked.

"Can't you read the sign? It says: HIJABS ONLY," Norjabeen shot back with a grin.

"Hey!" Mark exclaimed. "That's pretty good. You're funny. And pardon my dumb question, but where's your Middle Eastern accent?"

"My parents have been taking me to the U.S. for summers since I was five," Norjabeen responded. "Plus, I have plenty of relatives here, and my dad is originally from Michigan."

"Now I'm even more surprised you don't have an accent," Mark said. "There's a lot of people in Michigan who talk like they're from Canada."

"What if I told you I was half-Canadian?" Norjabeen said.

"Are you?" Mark asked.

"Nope."

"Ha, ha. Well then, maybe I can tell you my favorite Canada joke. I have an aunt from Toronto who told it to me."

"No thanks, Mark, I'm eating."

"Okay," Mark said, ignoring her. "Here it is: How many letters are there in 'Canada'?"

"Let me see. As many as the Canadian mail carriers can deliver," she replied.

"No, I mean how many letters are there in THE WORD 'Canada'?"

"That's easy," Norjabeen said. "Six-hundred, seventy-two."

"*Nooooooooo!*" Mark said. "Three. C, eh? N, eh? D, eh? Get it? Eh—A?" He drew a letter 'A' in the air to illustrate.

"This lunch is bad enough without the free comedy show," Norjabeen said. "Tepid, turkey corn dogs and greasy tempura broccoli spears. What were they thinking? No, I take that back—they *weren't* thinking. Zombies made this."

And so Mark and Norjabeen hit it off like the most unlikely of comic duos, which shocked the rest of Mark's lunch crowd. The two hardly noticed the spitballs and razzing, which died down in time. Then one day, they were joined by Noel Shea, one of the shy kids at the lunch table who'd had enough of the teasing. Noel's move opened up a floodgate. One by one, more kids came over to join them. And one by one, Norjabeen won them all over.

"So Norjabeen, what's really under the hijab?" asked one.

"I'm smuggling real food into the lunchroom, but it'll cost ya."

"Why do they call it a hijab?" asked another.

"Because hijab is hard to say, so you can't write any dumb rap songs about it."

"Is it true you're from Kuwait?"

"Let me dial into my home planet and see what I'm supposed to tell you. By the way, can you take me to your leader?"

In the meantime, Mark found himself inspired to do some amazing things. He was hanging out at the Famous Queen of Pizza one afternoon when he saw a table set up for sponsoring children through Transglobal Vision. He signed up not once but twice, deciding to support a six-year-old boy named Zakayo in Kenya and an eight-year-old girl named Natasha in Uzbekistan.

When Pastor Reynolds heard what Mark was doing with his allowance money, he invited him to speak at the pulpit during an upcoming Sunday service. This made Mark think that maybe he could recruit other sponsors as well. Though he was more used to joking than delivering impassioned speeches, he made a heartfelt case when he stepped up to speak.

"These kids may never know what it's like to go to a mall, or sleep in a cozy bedroom, or go an entire week without hunger pangs at night," Mark told the congregation. "And because they're so young, they can't help themselves. I've been called to stand up for kids like Zakayo and Natasha. Because if I don't stand up, it's only a matter of time before they fall down."

Afterwards, Mark signed up about 30 people, including Wendi. She smiled at him and said, "It took a lot of guts to get up there and speak—just like it took a lot of guts to sit down with Norjabeen at lunch."

"She's got a wicked sense of humor," Mark said. "Who knew?"

"Well, you know now," Wendi replied. "And I meant it. It took courage to stand up and walk over to her table. It takes courage to stand up, period. I never knew you had it in you."

"Neither did I," Mark said. "Maybe it was stuck inside and only came loose after you gave me a good kick in the butt."

"Anytime, Mark," Wendi said. "I'll supply the shoe. You supply the soul."

SCOOP TROOP ALERT

Wendi is right: Standing up for the weak and powerless takes courage. Although taking a stand can be scary, God gives us the strength we need. Who are some people or groups who are weak and powerless? Here are some ideas:

- People who are poor

- People with terminal illnesses

- People who have lost hope

- People who are hungry or homeless

- Victims of war

If you could stand up for anyone who is weak and powerless, who might that be? How would you do it? Who would you ask to join you in your effort?

Write about this and discuss it with your group. There is no pressure to take action—but if you feel the call to do so, be sure to discuss why you feel a call, and how you hope to answer it.

It's Raining Cats and Blogs

> *How can I make a difference?*
> **Care for God's creation.**

Posted April 1, by Wendi Best ("Prayergrrrl")

I know I'm taking a risk posting this blog entry on April Fools' Day, because there will be some people reading it who won't believe a thing I write. Two years ago, I won a bicycle in a drawing on April 1, and when I called my parents from the bike store to tell them the news, my mom hung up on me.

Even worse, Mark Engstrom could be reading this, Mr. Jolly Joker himself. So this is for you Mark: I truly, truly think your jokes are funnier than anything I could think up. April fool? You figure it out.

Now that that foolishness is out of the way... I want to talk about why this is a special occasion. A year ago today, my parents and I got Ethel from a greyhound rescue. She as a racing dog for most of her life and she's been through some tough times, which is why I think I identify with her.

Whenever things get really harsh around my house, and it isn't too dark out, I get Ethel leashed up, and we go for a run around the neighborhood. She may be old—she's almost

11 now—but she sure is fast. I can't imagine what it would've been like to run after her when she was still racing!

I convinced my parents to get her after I saw a TV special about the lives of racing greyhounds and how rescue operations help them to enjoy a tranquil "retirement." The dogs looked like such noble, graceful creatures to me—and when I went to meet Ethel at the shelter the following week, it was love at first bark. It sounds silly, but I could swear she kept scooping her long, long nose at me as if to say, "Hey! Wendi! Come here. I've got something to show you. Come on. Check this out!" And we've been best buds ever since. I'd never dye a pink streak in her coat, but I did just get her a spiked doggie collar. Too cute!

Monica has Mainframe, the computer. Christopher has his guitar. Rob has his sketch pad, and Mark has (what he thinks are) his jokes. Even Mr. Naynum has his bowling ball. But if you ask me, I've got it best of all. Ethel is the sixth-sense wonder dog; she always seems to know when I need cheering up or a big sloppy kiss on the cheek. Sometimes, she'll just park her ribsy frame next to me while I'm studying, and it's the greatest feeling. And if anyone so much as looks at me funny, she can growl and bark up a storm.

But that doesn't mean I'm exclusively a dog person. I have three cats too: Andes, my black short-haired Siamese; Butler, my furry gray Burmese; and Mouse, a fat orange Persian. (I thought it would be funny to name a cat Mouse. If I ever get a pet mouse, I'm naming it Kat. With a "K.") The one thing they have in common is that they were all castoffs— Andes was a stray, Butler was left behind by neighbors, and Mouse was given away as a kitten. I know what that's like, in a way. Being a part of a dysfunctional family will give you a good taste of what it's like to be left to twist in the wind: "Mom? Dad? Hello! I'm still here! Could you, like, save your fighting for when I'm not around?"

I can't stop my parents from arguing all the time, and it makes me mad. But part of being a punk-rock girl, and a *prayergrrrl*, is that I want to turn my anger into something productive. So instead of saying, "People are lousy, life stinks," I say, "No! What stinks is giving up." And so I spend time with the Scoop Troopers. I take care of my pets. And I try to be good to other people, especially anyone who's hurting and needing help.

Like this whole thing with Mark and Norjabeen. It blew me away when I saw Mark saying those things to her. I just couldn't stand to see him hurt Norjabeen like that. Under the force of peer pressure, Mark had let his potential to make a difference escape, although thankfully just temporarily. Some people would say they "don't want to interfere" or "get in people's way," but I see my actions as looking out for fellow children of God. I'd like to think other people would do the same thing for me.

I know I can't save the world, and I definitely don't try to. But it felt like I was making a big difference by helping Mark realize what he was doing to Norjabeen. Especially now. To see them hanging out, having fun, and other people joining in, I really feel like I did a good thing.

I know I have a bit of a hard shell, and I'm not the easiest person to get to know. I can be moody and tough—and frankly, I like to keep people at arm's length. But I care about God's creation. I really do. Just ask Ethel … who right now is licking my toes, which is making it REALLY HARD to finish this entry. Ethel! Stop!!! Hee, hee!

SCOOP TROOP ALERT

You have just read Wendi's blog entry. Now, pretend that you are one of her buddies on the Internet. Write Wendi a response that she can post on her home page. You can talk about anything, but try to stay focused on what she said in her entry, and the way it relates to her call (and yours) to care for God's creation.

You may want to share, for example, ways that you've found to protect and nurture God's creatures and children. Think about things that hold personal significance for you and remind you constantly how precious life is.

A "Love" Letter from Monica

> How can I make a difference?
> **Share the story of God's love.**

Newspapers have their slow and busy seasons, and those feverish times when a few reporters must tackle a very, very big backlog. Monica Perez didn't know what had caused it, but she did know was that her in-box was flooded with e-mail letters. Everyone wanted her advice—and as advice columnist for the *Good Newspaper*, her job was to dish it out.

Long after most of the other Scoop Troopers had gone home Sunday evening, Monica was still in the Shorewood Park Church basement, cranking out courtesy replies to reader mail—"Thanks for writing; I hope to get to your letter soon!"—and searching for just the right query to feature in her column. Only Rob Jordan was there to keep her company, and he had his headphones on and his face buried in his sketch pad.

"Okay, Mainframe, call up letter 46," Monica said, her voice a bit frayed.

"Coming up, Monica!" said Mainframe in that movie star voice swiped from the suave actor, Donny Sheek.

"Mainframe, Mainframe, Mainframe," Monica said. "Is it possible you could use some other voice? Like maybe Winston Churchill? Or the announcer from the Mocha Madness commercials? Or even a woman? Just wondering."

"Is it possible," Mainframe replied, "that you could turn green and croak like a bullfrog? I am who my creator made me to be, microchips and all."

"A philosophical computer," Monica marveled. "Try finding that at some electronics superstore."

"Indeed!" Mainframe exclaimed. "And now, letter number 46." The words flashed onto the screen and Monica began to read them aloud:

Dear Monica:

I need your help. I love God so much. But when it comes to sharing the story of God's love, I get all tongue-tied. Sometimes I feel too dumb to find the right words to say. And other times, I feel like I'm preaching at people if I say too much. So mostly, I keep my mouth shut. But that doesn't seem right either. I feel like no matter what I do, I'm messing up. And I wonder if God is disappointed in me. How can I make it up to him?

Sincerely,

Janey Garner

Monica was moved. She leaned back in her chair and watched Rob sketch away, his pencil skating across the paper as he listened to hip-hop music (with the volume cranked so loud she heard tinny drum machine beats spilling from his headphones). She pondered for a few moments, then smiled and began to type.

This is what Monica wrote:

Dear Janey:

First of all, just as much as you love God, God loves you a million times more. There is no way you can disappoint Jesus, unless you turn away from him. You do not have to earn his love. That's not how it works. Jesus gave his life for you, and all he asks in return is that you accept his gift. You are his child. He loves you! Nothing can change that.

That is the heart of your story—and ours. And as for how to share the story of God's love, I have several ideas that may help. For starters, if you're worried about how your words come out, start by showing God's love before telling about it. Help out a person in need. Be loving and warm to the ones Jesus called "the least of these." Use your gifts wisely and make this world—or even your classroom—a better place. Without sounding too cliché, just look around you! Make God's love visible to others through the things you do.

When you are ready to share the story of God's love, remember that it's love—so speak from the heart. Talk about what Jesus has done for you. Share the tough times your faith has helped you to weather. Most people who get in trouble sharing their faith are just plain pushy. They take a "my way or the highway" approach. Where's the love in that?

And if you're worried that you're talking too much, listen. Listen to the person you're with, even when they tell you all the reasons they find it hard to believe in

God. Maybe they're used to Christians being judgmental and not taking the time to understand them. Love is listening! We know God listens to our prayers, right? So listen to others before you choose to share. It's not just what you say but how—and when—you choose to say it.

A few more things: Throw out the script. Don't judge your performance. And don't worry about trying to "score points" or achieve a goal. Love never keeps score and neither does Jesus.

Your friend in Christ,

Monica Perez

Monica scrolled through the copy after she typed it. It felt right. She'd poured her own love into it. Still, she felt as if something was missing.

"Rob? Rob?! ROB!!!" Monica had to shout to get his attention. He shut off the music and looked up.

"Rob, can you take a look at this advice column for the *Good Newspaper*? I think it's finished, but I'm wondering if it needs something. A finishing touch, maybe."

"Sure," Rob said. He walked over to Mainframe and read the draft. He nodded his head. He paused and nodded again. "Uh-huh. Uh-huh."

"So?"

"Looks great, Monica. And you're right. There *is* something missing."

"So, what is it?" Monica asked. She was dying to know what else she could possibly say.

Rob trotted back to his sketch pad and flipped over to a

clean page. Using a black marker, he made a simple sketch like the kind the pop artist Keith Haring might do: no facial features, no shading, just lines. It depicted Jesus gathering a little child in his outstretched arms.

"It needs this," Rob said.

Monica looked at the sketch, then at Rob, then at the sketch again. It took him all of two minutes to complete, but Monica felt its impact would last far, far longer than that.

"Quick, put it away," Monica said, "before I start to cry all over it."

"You like it, then?" Rob asked, smiling.

"What's the old saying? Your picture is worth 1,000 words," Monica replied. "And then some."

SCOOP TROOP ALERT

Here's your chance to tell your story of God's love!

Get a large piece of paper and the drawing implements of your choice—pens, markers, pastels, colored pencils, or a mix. Now, draw a map—one that depicts the major events of your life. It could take the form of a path, a series of images, or a comic book panel. The choice is up to you.

Now, place a special symbol (a star, a cross, a heart—your choice) next to times you felt God's love and presence the most.

As you think about the ways God has made his love visible to you, consider how this may change the way you share stories of God with others. There's nothing like a personal account—especially if you're relating it to someone who knows you and cares about you—to grab someone's attention. A word often used in the church for this is "testimony," and it's a valuable way that faith gets passed down.

I Will Follow

> How can I make a difference?
>
> **Follow Jesus.**

"Mr. Naynum! Mr. Naynum!" Christopher exclaimed as he rushed into the basement of Shorewood Park Church, a full hour before the next Scoop Troop meeting. "I need your advice. Well, actually I don't—but someone very close to me does."

Mr. Naynum, sitting at his desk, cast a puzzled look. Christopher was a perfectly nice kid, but he hardly asked for input on anything except what page to place an article in the *Good Newspaper*. Wendi? That was a given—she sought his counsel all the time. Monica? She treated him like the uncle she wished she'd always had. But Christopher was so laid back, sometimes he wondered if the kid wasn't aloof or even a bit smug. *Banish the thought,* Mr. Naynum said to himself. *Christopher needs you. Listen.*

"I'm all ears," Mr. Naynum replied. "What can I do?"

"Well, it's my brother Ben," Christopher said. "He taught me how to play guitar, you know, and now his songs have attracted the attention of some really important music business people. And he's only 19! They want him to record his songs and maybe go on a short tour this summer."

"That sounds fantastic!" Mr. Naynum said. "So far, I don't hear any tough challenge—though from the tone of your voice, there must be one."

Christopher sighed. "There sure is. Ben writes about all sorts of things: love, sleeping late, the mountains. He even wrote a song about an orange on a dare. Now the people who've heard his music want to know if he can do Christian songs too. And I think it's a fantastic opportunity."

"But?" Mr. Naynum asked.

"Ben isn't 100 percent sure," Christopher said. "He wonders if it would be right for him to write songs about Jesus and faith just because he might be able to get a tour out of it. And he's worried that if the songs aren't good enough, he'll feel like he's been forced into something he's not comfortable doing. He's plenty excited. But he wants to get it right, and he's not sure where to begin or what to do. Plus, he's worried about selling out just because this is good exposure for his music. He's scared of doing the wrong thing."

Mr. Naynum rested his chin in his left hand and thought a moment. This sure was a unique dilemma. Most performers who do Christian songs would be worried about selling out if they decided to sing about everyday stuff. But here was a kid who was concerned about doing the same thing if he went Christian with his music, in part because someone dangled a carrot in front of him. *Ben sure has a lot of integrity,* he thought.

"Okay, Christopher," Mr. Naynum said. "I'm not sure if this is the best advice because you know, I'm not 100 percent certain what I would do! But I'm going to try. You ready?"

Christopher got out a note pad and pen. "Sure."

Mr. Naynum laughed. "You don't have to take notes, Christopher. My advice is simple enough. It's not so much *what* Ben does as *the heart* he does it with—and whether he's following God's call or something else."

"I think I see, but can you explain?" Christopher asked.

"It's like this: You could be a Christian musician who's

dishonest because you write and perform songs about God without any faith or commitment behind them. Or you could be a performer who's called to praise and worship in song, but chooses to do shallow music because you're chasing fame and fortune. Either way, the question is: Are you doing your best to obey God?"

"Wow," Christopher said. "But it sure would be easier if God was down here with a sign pointing in the right direction."

"God is, in a way," Mr. Naynum said. "It's not about choosing one kind of music over another. Should he do disco or rock? Jazz or polkas? God loves all kinds. But I would think that the music he loves most of all is anything made to glorify him. Take that rock band U2. They did a song a long time ago called 'I Will Follow.' It's pretty spiritual, but it's a song loved by Christians and non-Christians alike."

"Ben loves U2," Christopher said.

"You know about the classical composer Bach, right?"

"Sure."

"He signed all of his compositions, 'To the Glory of God Alone.' *Soli Deo Gloria.* Powerful stuff, if you ask me."

"Hey! I have an idea!" Christopher said. "What if Ben wrote Christian songs from his own perspective, performed some of his favorite hymns and worship songs, and continued to write about all sorts of other topics like he does now, from a Christian point of view?"

"Now you're talking!" Mr. Naynum said. "You see, God doesn't place boundaries on our creativity. God's love is limitless. And we are made in God's image. We're not meant to confine ourselves when it comes to making God's love shine through song, art, or even sports—especially bowling!"

Christopher laughed.

"And another thing, Christopher. God needs good musicians—not just good missionaries and pastors. God needs good teachers, too. Good performers. Good secretaries. People who bring so much care and concern to what they do that the love pours out of them like a floodlight."

"Now I'm excited!" Christopher said. "I can't wait to tell Ben what you've said. See ya, Mr. Naynum." He reached over and gave him a quick hug.

Mr. Naynum was going to mention something about coming back anytime, but Christopher was gone so fast he couldn't get the words out. It was silent except for the random hissing and clanging of a stuck radiator. A hug from Christopher? What next?

Just then Mainframe the computer clicked on with a whir of a hard drive.

"Mr. Naynum?"

"Yes, Mainframe?"

"I require your wise human guidance..."

George Naynum, mentor to man and machine, he thought to himself, chuckling.

SCOOP TROOP ALERT

Your assignment is to outline a situation in your life, current or in the near future, where you're not sure of the right way to go. Describe it in as much detail as you can.

In one column, put THE CHALLENGE.

In a second, put OPTIONS AND QUESTIONS.

In a third, put WAYS I CAN FOLLOW GOD.

Fill in the columns as best you can. Save the chart when you are done and use it to monitor your progress as you work through the situation.

SCOOP TROOP ALERT

How do we know what the right thing is, and how to follow God? Mr. Naynum told Christopher that God does point in the right direction—if you know where to look for signs. Where do we find those?

SCRIPTURE: Reading the Bible is a great way to see how people throughout time have faced problems and dilemmas similar to your own.

MENTORS: Mentors have the benefit of experience. They probably have been down the road you're on—or something close to it.

COMMUNITY: Loving community members will never force you to do something because of peer pressure, popularity, or an agenda meant to override your concerns and emotions. What they will do is listen and stay with you.

Epilogue

Where Do We Grow from Here?

● ● ● ● ● ● ● ● ● ● ●

Wendi couldn't help thinking about it as the Scoop Troopers hiked up to Sunrise Peak for an outdoor picnic-meeting: Whenever spring comes, the daylight may grow longer, but the days seem to go faster. There's giddiness in the air, but sadness too; spring gives way to summer and the final school bell sounds, sending everyone screaming on their way to whatever plans and dreams vacation may hold. Gardens burst in radiant glory, but the schoolyard goes silent and still. The warmth returns, but school-day friendships hibernate as if sealed in the dark, empty hallways of Hinton Heights Middle School.

But at least the Scoop Troopers, she assured herself, would stick together. As much as Mark could annoy her with his jokes, or Monica with her control-freak tendencies, or Rob with his philosophical ramblings, or Christopher with his air-headedness, they were her friends—and she cared for them all. Besides, she knew she could be annoying too. *I guess we're all a bit strange,* she thought. *But at least we're not strangers.*

"Ouch! Hey, Monica!!!" Mark complained as he lugged a large picnic basket up a steep grassy slope. "What did you pack in here? Whole watermelons? No wait, I know—everything we need for a pig roast—including the pig."

"Now, now, Mark," Monica said. "You can't have a proper picnic without the food. And the utensils. And the napkins. And the peach cobbler. And the beverages. And…"

"A do-it-yourself kit to—*rrrrggg!*—build a tractor trailer," Mark interrupted, grunting and tugging.

"Do you need help?" Christopher asked. "I could grab one handle with my left hand and carry my guitar case with my right." Monica's heart skipped a beat to hear Christopher giving such a generous offer.

Just then Mr. Naynum stepped over and took the basket from Mark, gently but with a firm enough grasp to convince him to let go. "It's okay, Mark," he said, smiling.

"Thanks, Mr. Naynum!" said Mark, gasping. "Look at my hands. I feel like I've been holding on to the stretched rubber band in David's slingshot for about three hours."

"I don't think they had rubber bands back then," Rob said, lugging a cooler with a lopsided waddle.

"I wonder if they had bad jokes then," Wendi said. "In which case Mark would've been a shoo-in for numerous Bible references. But who knows? Maybe he would've wrangled his way into a job at Pharaoh's court and driven him crazy. Then he wouldn't have been able to let Moses' people go, and they'd *still* be in captivity today."

"Some people would define 'captivity' as a state of mind," Mark responded. "Especially when it's exhibited by a certain girl with pink hair and punk tastes."

"I'm gonna miss this," Rob said.

"*Waaait* a minute. What are you talking about Rob?" Wendi said. "First of all, I haven't had a chance to respond to Mark's last comment and put him in his place. Then you say, 'I'm going to miss this.' What gives, Sketchman?"

"Uhm, I didn't want to say anything..." Rob began.

"When does he ever want to say anything? Unless it's the ultimate brain tease," Christopher whispered to Monica.

"...but my uncle in Tokyo has invited me to spend the summer with him. And I think I'm gonna say 'yes.'"

"ROB!" Wendi exclaimed. "You can't! I mean, you can, but..."

"Okay, confession time for me, too," Christopher said. "My brother Ben is hitting the road for a six-week, mini-tour of coffeehouses and churches. My mom plans on coming, and Ben's asked me to be his roadie."

"This can't be happening," Wendi said.

"What's going to become of the *Good Newspaper*?" Monica asked. "Mr. Naynum? Mr. Naynum?"

"Well," Mr. Naynum said. "It *is* summer. What are you going to do?"

"Don't tell me you're going away too!" Wendi said. It was all she could do to keep from losing it right then and there. It felt like total abandonment.

"Look," Mr. Naynum said. "Everyone's going to be back in September, God willing. Rob will come home from Japan. Christopher will return from the music tour. And by then..."

"What?" Wendi asked, her face blank with disbelief.

"By then I'll be back from my cross-country motorcycle trip," Mr. Naynum said.

Wendi burst into tears. The other Scoop Troopers, as if by instinct, gathered around her.

Mr. Naynum stood just outside the circle, his hands sheltering the kids as if he were blessing them. No one said a word for a few minutes; Wendi did her best to stifle her sobbing and regain her composure. She reached into her pocket, grabbed a tissue, and blew her nose hard.

"Okay," she said stepping away, her eyes raw. "I'm fine. I'm fine. No more crying. So, tell us about your trip, Mr. Naynum." She was doing her best to be stoic, but her hands shook as she looked at him.

Mr. Naynum saw this and lowered his voice as if to calm and console. "Wendi, I've always, always wanted to do this. I mentioned it to my mother as recently as two years ago. She was a worrier, I'll tell you. But you know what? She encouraged me to go for it. 'Do it son, because life is short and dreams have a habit of slipping away,' she said. But then she got really sick, and all of my energy went to taking care of her. Now that she's no longer around, I feel this strong pull to go—it's as if she's whispering in my ear."

"I'm scared," Wendi said. "Is this the end of the Scoop Troop? If you guys aren't around, how am I going to know what to do when my parents fight for the one-thousandth time or I have a problem or I'm afraid of losing my temper? How will I make the right choices? How am I going to keep growing in my faith?"

"I know it's hard to accept that this is goodbye," Mr. Naynum said. "But not for long. And not forever. Nothing can separate us. That's what Momma said to me before she passed on: 'Nothing can separate us.' And I feel her presence closer to me than ever right now."

"We can always send e-mail," Christopher offered.

"And I'll still be around," Mark said. "You wanna hear a bad joke? Maybe if I tell you what I think is a bad joke, you'll actually think it's good."

Wendi laughed.

"Seeeeee?" Mark said.

"And I'll send you the best postcards you've ever seen, Wendi, because I'll draw them myself! Promise," Rob said.

"You know," Christopher said, "I'm afraid too, Wendi. I'll be away from home and in a different city or town just about every night. Nothing will look familiar. A lot of it will be boring. And if Ben calls me on stage to play with him, I have no idea what I'll do. But your number is programmed into my cell phone speed dial. I hope you'll take my calls."

"Of course," Wendi said.

The kids reached the top of Sunrise Peak, the afternoon sky fired with hues of pink and burnt vermilion. The view of Shorewood below was glorious, the houses and streets spread out like a board game layout.

"Come on!" Monica said. "Let's picnic! Isn't anyone hungry? Let's throw down the blanket and get down to business!!!" Monica seemed unusually cheery, her smile and demeanor forced.

Wendi called her on it. "Monica, we know what everyone will be up to this summer—except you. What's the scoop, Scoop Trooper?"

Monica seemed nervous. "Just another boring summer for me," she said. "Lots of swimming and reading and maybe a little gardening and..."

"Come on, Monica. 'Fess up," Wendi said. "I'll be here running my greyhound around the neighborhood, and I'm afraid of the Scoop Troop breaking up. What's going on with you?"

Monica sighed. "My dad ... you would think that with my summer vacation around the corner, my dad would make an effort to spend some time with me. Then I hear that he and his wife are off to France to do a bicycle tour. As if *I* don't love to bike too!"

"I had no idea," Wendi said.

What Monica didn't say was that she felt almost as bad about Christopher going away for the summer. Christopher Lewis, whom she'd grown so fond of that she hoped the two of them would become "an item," as they say around Hinton Heights.

So Wendi feels abandoned? What about me? Monica thought to herself.

"Is there still time to put out a last issue?" Monica asked, passing fried chicken out to everyone. "This was originally supposed to be a Scoop Troop meeting, not a Last Supper."

"Where do we grow from here?" Christopher asked.

"That's it!" Monica said. "That's what we can write about! How do we move forward in our faith when we feel uncertain and alone, and how do we step out in faith?"

"Did I just come up with another good idea without knowing it?" Christopher said.

"It beats cracking a good joke without remembering it," Mark said. "I said something a few days ago that cracked up everyone in my home room, but I can't recall what it was."

"I know," Wendi said. "I think it was ... *uhmmm* ... 'Laugh if you think I'm unfunny.' "

"HA ... HA ... HA," Mark said, drawing out his laughter to sound like a bored robot.

The Scoop Troopers spent the rest of that afternoon talking, planning, joking, playing Frisbee, and wondering how summer would unfold without the Scoop Troop as a sanctuary. No one would miss the dusty basement of Shorewood Park Church, they agreed—though all would miss the good times that had taken place there.

"Do you think they can get rid of that worn carpet and the stale tile?" Monica asked Mr. Naynum. "And put in some fresh curtains?"

He laughed. "I agree, it's a pit down there, Monica! I'll see what I can do."

The afternoon light hazed over and faded. The Scoop Troopers packed up the basket and cooler, folded up the blanket, and agreed to meet later that night at Seven-Ten Lanes for a farewell round of bowling. Mr. Naynum announced that he would treat, and the Troopers rushed up to give him a hug.

"Father, watch over these brothers and sisters in Christ as they head off into a summer that we hope is full of wonder and promise and joy," Mr. Naynum prayed. "We thank you for the fellowship that binds us and the community that nurtures us. Your love sustains us, allows us to go out into the world and be your lights, shunning the darkness and illuminating the doorway that welcomes others into your midst. Let us always remember to love one another as you love us. And we pray that your will be done as we set our eyes on the autumn, when we all hope to join hands and hearts again. Amen."

Later that day, as Monica got dressed for the bowling night, she opened her purse, looking for a brush. She tipped it over and a note fell out.

It was a card with her name on it.

Monica opened it. And she smiled as she read:

Monica,

It's been great getting to know you. If it weren't for you, I'd never have gotten to go on this Scoop Troop adventure. Maybe it was my idea to start a newspaper, but you were the one who recognized it and promoted it. Admit it.

Will think of you often on the road. Be sure to save the coupon inside. It's good for one milkshake, my treat, when I get back from the tour.

Your friend (and maybe more)—

Christopher

"Yesssssssss!!!!!!" Monica shouted.

Saying goodbye is hard. Going forward without the support of friends or loved ones nearby is even harder. What do you do when you are alone and afraid? How do you stay centered in your faith? And how would you encourage others who are faced with the same situation? Here, the object is simple: Find a tale from your own faith walk where you were forced to confront and transcend your fears and isolation. How were you able to stay centered and move ahead? And what important lessons did you learn that you would want to pass down?